TIPS

for

TIME TRAVELERS

TIPS
for

Peter Cochrane

TIME TRAVELERS

MCGRAW-HILL

NEW YORK   SAN FRANCISCO   WASHINGTON, D.C.   AUCKLAND   BOGATÁ
CARACAS   LISBON   LONDON   MADRID   MEXICO CITY   MILAN
MONTREAL   NEW DELHI   SAN JUAN   SINGAPORE
SYDNEY   TOKYO   TORONTO

Library of Congress Cataloging-in-Publication Data

Cochrane, Peter.
    Tips for time travelers / Peter Cochrane.
        p.   cm.
    Includes bibliographical reference and index.
    ISBN 0-07-012070-6
     I. Technological forecasting. 2. Technology—Social aspects.
  I. Title.
  T174.C63 1998
  303.48'3—dc21   98-37193
                                   CIP

McGraw-Hill

A Division of The **McGraw-Hill** Companies

First published by The Orion Publishing Group Ltd London.

1 2 3 4 5 6 7 8 9 0 DOC/DOC 9 0 3 2 1 0 9 8

ISBN 0-07-012070-6

The sponsoring editor for this book was David Bernstein, the editing supervisor was Paul R. Sobel, and the production supervisor was Modestine Cameron. The designer was Michael Mendelsohn and the text was set in Triplex Serif Light by MM Design 2000, Inc.

Printed and bound by R. R. Donnelley & Sons Company.

McGraw-Hill books are available at special quantity discounts to use as premiums and sales promotions, or for use in corporate training programs. For more information, please write to the Director of Special Sales, McGraw-Hill, 11 West 19th Street, New York, NY 10011. Or contact your local bookstore.

This book is printed on recycled, acid-free paper containing a minimum of 50% recycled, de-inked fiber.

For Brenda,
my closest and most trustworthy
time traveler

CONTENTS

To boldly go and be first . . .

Today I enjoy the privilege of being the head of Europe's fore-most telecommunication research laboratory in one of the world's most successful companies, British Telecom (BT). In this role I get to meet some of the most outstanding thinkers, scientists, engineers, politicians, artists, and humanists alive today. I also get to steer, originate, and participate in some of the most radical research focused on a future 10 to 50 years out. But it was not always so. . .

In 1957 I was 11 years old, and a childhood illness confined me to bed for over six weeks. Unbeknown to me at that time, this was to be a key turning point in my life and the start of a life-long love affair with technology. A few simple experiments using pipe cleaners, cycle bulbs, and batteries on my bed covers soon saw me making Morse lamps and spark transmitters. To the bemusement of friends and family, with my recovered health I began collecting old radio sets to extend my experiments into hi-fi, amateur radio, and radio-controlled aircraft. Throughout this period my mother had to put up with my bedroom looking like the local scrap heap, while my father would help me all he could with the rudimentary knowledge gained as an engine fitter in the RAF during WWII. Today, I look back and can only salute their forbearance and support.

With little or no guidance and tutoring, my progress was slow, but my ignorance of engineering and scientific detail often allowed me to make giant conceptual leaps, and I most certainly took some substantial risks. The possibility of electrocution was never far away in those heady days of 300-500V power supplies, but I survived. Unfortunately, my basic education and social environment were at odds with this direction of thought and experience, for I had been born into a coalmining community in Nottinghamshire. Here there was no expectation other than to learn what was taught and be the son of a miner, or if you were really bright, a sales assistant in a local store. At that time and place everyone's horizon was both very close and very limited.

I had struggled through my formative years and emerged from school at 15 years old not knowing what a logarithm was, unread and poorly prepared for a world of work, but I could build amplifiers and radios. I had worked in the local radio store for more than a year and had developed an intuitive and green-fingered approach to the location and repair of faults. In 1961 all I wanted was a chance to work in that store. This was my dream. I was besotted by the technology of thermionic tubes, and the early transistor. But times were hard and there was no prospect of a full-time position, so I attended a further year at college studying a wide range of basic engineering skills, from machining metal, welding, braising, and soldering to machines and basic design.

At 16 years old the General Post Office (GPO) looked kindly on me and gave me a job as a trainee telephone technician. In 1962 I was digging holes in the road, putting up poles, installing telephones, repairing systems, and learning exciting things about electromechanical switches. Being a government institution and an enlightened organization by the standards of that time, the GPO packed me off on residential training courses and regular day and night school classes. A new world opened before me. I had become thirsty for knowledge, full of questions born of the half-truths and partial understanding gained from my wholly practical excursions into the world of physics and engineering. Working hard turned out to be fun, because the area presented a new form of intoxication. At 19 I was attending technical school classes every night and one day a week, rapidly making up for the wasted years of my early education.

At this point three factors came into play to again change the course of my life forever. First, the GPO employed some wonderful technical staff who would take young people under their wing, nurture, educate, and help anyone who showed the least amount of interest. In my case that amounted to an infinity of questions, experimentation, and learning. I later discovered from others that I had a disarming ability to rationalize complex situations and find the shortest route to a solution. Second, I became the student of a retired high school teacher who took it upon himself to sort out my mathematical difficulties forever, and he did a superb job and empowered me for life. Third, in 1965 I met my wife-to-be, Brenda, and I became even more motivated to strive for a far brighter and interesting future. My pivotal moment came in 1968 when I was accepted on an Electrical Engineering Degree Course at Nottingham Polytechnic. This defining epoch set my trajectory for life; I was to become an engineer, scientist, technologist, and manager. Within five years I had a first-class BS honors degree, two years later an MS, and two years after that, in 1979, a PhD. Most important, I had a deep engineering and scientific understanding and some wonderful role models for the rest of my life.

Returning to the GPO Research Department saw me programming early mainframe computers in machine code and working on switching, test, and measurement systems. However, it was my move into cable transmission and the development of fibre optic systems that created my next acceleration in thinking and experience. Designing for subocean depths in excess of 4 km and system operation lifetimes of 25 years presented a challenge comparable to getting someone to the moon. I also had the good fortune to be involved in data modem design, human speech processing, test equipment development, radio and cable systems, and the design and manufacture of ultra reliable chips for undersea use.

Throughout this 20-year period I continued to teach at universities in the UK and abroad and had built up a considerable experience as an international consultant. My wife and I had been fortunate to have a family of three children, which eclipses all the efforts of my professional life. In 1984 the GPO was privatized, set free of government control as a new company, British Telecom (BT). Among the many changes were a rapid staff downsizing of 50 percent in just six years and a 150 percent increase in R&D. The main board of this new company had realized that radical change was needed if BT was to survive and prosper. On 26 August 1987, I was promoted to head the Long Lines Research Division at the heyday of fibre optic developments, and on that same day Brenda gave birth to our fourth and last child. Just four years later in 1991 I was singled out and invited to build a new Research Department to explore and map out the future of technology and humankind. The most exciting phase of my life to date had begun.

Starting with just a secretary and an office, I formulated a dream, a vision of the future that could be built and experienced, a testbed for people, where technology would do our bidding or be extinguished. To recruit the best people available, I set up a global lecture circuit selling this vision of living ahead of everyone else, exploiting technology, and exploring where others had not been. My mission statement, coined in 1991, is still in place today:

> *To boldly go and be first; technologically, managerially, and operationally.*

The vision and purpose statement is also still in place:

> *To create the core competencies for the future, and ensure BT is never wrong footed by technological, market or social change.*

As an extension of best practice, I also engaged in formulating a framework of ethics and responsibilities to ensure the groundbreaking direction of this research would encompass some essential safeguards.

These included:

Responsibilities to mankind, society, the company, profession, colleagues, families and ourselves.
Complete and positive openness and collaboration with all interested parties within and without the industry, company and nation. This to be constrained only by commercial imperatives and national security.

During this early period I incessantly read books on biology and life systems, psychology, mathematics, chaos, economics, politics, law, philosophy, medicine, art and science fiction. I also travelled to the leading laboratories and companies worldwide, talked and met with many of the greatest thinkers, and sat in lectures and attended conferences. Among the guiding principles I formulated was the decision to avoid all existing research areas, to do or attempt nothing any other research group was doing. It had also become clear to me that our world was undergoing a transition from a reasonably well-behaved place dominated by random events to a world of chaos (in the mathematical sense of the word) and correlated behavior on a massive scale. In fact, it was clear that the domination of atoms was nearly over and our future would be bit-dominated. Information would be the next "king."

Most upsetting of all, I could see that much of our mathematical and physical understanding was a of little or no value in this new regime of bits and chaos. This became clear while playing with a colony of ants in a Spanish gutter. Here were animals with only 200 neurons and about 400 lines of high-level code of such collective ability and resilience. Kill one ant, a hundred, or thousands, and the colony self-heals and continues to function. In contrast, remove a comma or full stop from our software, cut a wire, or pull a single chip at random and our networks and computer systems collapse. Moving on to jellyfish, slime mould and other insects, I became increasingly impressed by the minimalistic engineering of Mother Nature. The lack of any central control or intelligence being a key feature along with low flat hierarchies. Pursuing this line of investigation I gradually became aware of the order of intelligence and society of minds at work in everything we do. Our societal pecking order and need for control and domination of everything seems to have infested all our engineering and system thinking to an unreasonable degree. Right out of the blue, I asked a colleague to build an ant colony, which took little more than a week. I then set up a team to tackle a major network software problem. Within a few months they had replaced 1,600,000 lines of code with a mere 1000, and a new development path was established.

During this seminal period I also began to see a growing inappropriateness of existing government, societal, and commercial institutions for the future world, and a growing potential for destabilization. My path was clear: artificial life, intelligence, war-gaming and modeling, and machine-human interfaces would form the core activities of my new research laboratory. This stark realization and the programs it engendered saw the laboratory grow to 60 people in year one, to more than 120 at the end of year two, and today it is more than 600 full-time members of staff, supplemented with over 300 visiting students, academicians, and fellows. In turn, they feed technology and knowledge in support of over 6000 development staff focused on the sharp end of the BT business.

What followed was even more remarkable. My teams developed intelligent agents capable of navigating nets, while simultaneously learning about our likes and dislikes, needs and desires. When combined with artificial life and software reproduction, this realized new inroads to the holy grail of artificial intelligence. Today, we have a range of products at the prototype stage that include computer and telephone interfaces that bend to our individual ways of working and very intelligent mobile terminals. We have also created network and system algorithms that are unsurpassed in the reliability they realize with ever-greater hardware and software efficiency.

By inflicting such leading-edge technology on ourselves—a 1000+ research team using everyone as a guinea pig, we have been able to steer a path through a multiplicity of technology options. It is hard to find any part or product of BT that we have not influenced in some way. Everything from network design, software algorithms, wearable computers, chip implants, Intranets, telemedicine, teleconferencing, teleeducation, agents, e-commerce and security, iris recognition systems, and working practices bear our mark of influence. Our creation, a world 10 years ahead of most people, is liveable and delightful, but not without its dangers.

This book documents many of the early experiences, discoveries, and findings of my laboratory during the past six years. These have been selected because they are most likely to impact on Joe Public at home and at work in the not-too-distant future. This book was never intended to be a deep scientific work aimed at the professional and student. It is a book for everyone struggling with the rapidly accelerating pace of life and impacted by technologies that increasingly look like magic. It is a book by me and of me, personally, and is not a corporate view. Indeed, many people in BT do not always agree with me, but to their great credit the BT Board; Sir Iain Vallance, my Chairman; and my direct boss, Dr. Alan Rudge, have always lent me every support and enough freedom to impact on both the company and society. Without their support we could not have gained the insights you are about to discover in this volume or the tremendous depth of knowledge hidden within the perimeter fence of complexity surrounding an increasingly chaotic world.

For most Americans BT is synonymous with MCI and a failed merger bid in 1997. Perhaps the company looks just like any other foreign predator in a rapidly changing market. In reality, it is much more, being unique among all the telcos of the world in its approach to the business of change and the need to understand the complexities of the future. As one of the largest groups in the sector, it has for many years been the most profitable. For me, it has always been a privilege to be a part of this organization and more recently a primary agent of change, backed by an outstanding and very talented research team. I have learned so much from so many people, but I have also learned a lot from living in the future. Who knows? This may not turn out to be just a book about the future, but a book of the future. Either way, it is my purpose to forewarn and forearm you, the reader, for a future of ever more technology.

As my friend Alan Kay once commented:

"You cannot predict the future, but you can build it."

In the future there is man, woman, and machine, a partnership of carbon- and silicon-based life and intelligence with technology augmenting and enhancing our species. There is profound change to all aspects of society, with chips in everything, ubiquitous computing and rapid communication over global networks, easy access to information and experience, and technologies that are mostly as-well-as, but sometimes instead-of. Like the basket weavers, potters, and scribes of old, machines will take over many human tasks and create even more new ones. What we did in the past to earn money we may well take on as a hobby as technology gives us an ever-wider choice. It is not a future to be feared but to be embraced for the huge benefits it will bring. This text contains many reminders to technologists that they have a primary responsibility to society and the planet. Creating technologies that are sustainable, humanized, and easy to use and offering far more opportunities for good than harm have to be foremost in our objectives. It is possible, and it can be done . . .

Enjoy,

Peter Cochrane
40,000 ft over the South China Sea

This may be the most unusual book you ever buy or read. The content, format. purpose, and style are unconventional by design, to meet the needs of time travellers—us. It was written on planes, trains, and in the backs of cars as I travelled through time and space. Most of the content has appeared in a weekly column in the UK *Daily Telegraph* and other newspapers and magazines, plus radio and TV interviews worldwide.

So you might well ask: Why put it all in a book? Well, it is all part of an experiment in communication and meme propagation—and not everyone is on line, buys a newspaper, watches TV, or listens to the radio. Besides paper is still a very user-friendly technology and part of a multimedia world.

Thirty years ago I could have found time to read *War & Peace* or any other tome. Even 10 years ago, I might have attempted such a laborious process, but not any more. I just cannot find the time to work through 10 x 30-page (or more) chapters, let alone two are three chapters in one go. So this book is written and organized in subject bytes of about 600 words. These 24kByte monologues can be read in "5 minutes as you wait for a cab, have lunch, a coffee, an Internet download, or perhaps more likely as you journey by car, train, or plane. With the most adverse reading conditions and the busiest people in mind, the font, point, and line-spacing have been purposely selected to minimize the need for good lighting and the onset of motion sickness.

This is a book for anyone interested in or concerned about the future, especially those ultrabusy people (time travellers) traversing the planet as atoms or bits to create wealth and transform society and life. All the content is drawn from the real-life experiences of someone living on the edge of the IT dream, an on-line human with a family, a full-time job, responsibilities, and enough real and virtual space, but not enough time. In fact, I am just someone trying to survive and cope with a world of exponential change. I'm a lover of technology and people and a hater of bad design and unfriendly interfaces.

Each monologue is self-contained, and they can be read in any order. There seems to be no logical way to order the subject matter, so I made no effort to do so. However, the monologues are numbered from 1 to 108 and there is an index at the back to facilitate a keyword search should you need to find relevant material or a route to meme linking. When you have bought, read, or sampled this book, you may wish to visit my home page to discover much more material and depth:

http://www.labs.bt.com/people/cochrap

This collection of bytes is a product of working and meeting with people and technology in my parent organization British Telecom; of being a consultant to industry and government;and of being an educator and technology prophet. All have played an important part in shaping my thoughts and ideas as we have struggled to find solutions to problems and second guess progress. It is also a result of living during the 52 most exciting years the human race has seen. If I had the choice, I would wind back my body clock by 30 years, take my brain with me, and continue my time travels even further than I shall be naturally allowed. For you, the reader I hope to have preempted some of the changes you will experience very soon. Enjoy!

Peter Cochrane

ACKNOWLEDGMENTS

Since this book is the product of working with hundreds and meeting with thousands of people over my life to date, it is impossible to name everyone I am indebted to. But I feel I should at least mention those directly involved in the most recent production process. John Browning of *Wired UK* and Robin Hunt of the Guardian Newspaper Group deserve special mention for originally inviting me to write for them some four years ago. Ben Rooney is my current editor at the *Daily Telegraph* and has been another key player in encouraging me to write and be ultra-productive. I well remember him asking me to write a one-year series of 52 monologues for *Connected@Telegraph* and worrying about my ability to find even the first 10 topics to write about. However, once I got started, one topic after another just seemed to pop into my head, and Ben has never seen fit to significantly massage my drafts or change my messages. He has simply encouraged and gently steered the development of these articles from time to time.

Martin Liu of Orion Books cold-called me by e-mail one February day in 1997, and we had our first meeting in the Housemaster's office at St. Dunstan's College in Catford, London, just before I gave the 1997 Armstrong Society Lecture. From the outset, he moved very quickly to reach an agreement, formulate a plan, and kick the process of production into gear. At this point, my youngest daughter, Sarah, took charge of me and made sure I did all the right things on time and in the right style. She also did quite a job as the proofreader, subeditor, agent, and manager.

As a direct result of David Evans inviting me to the October 1997 *Business Week* Conference in Paris, Harry Somerdyk put me in touch with Philip Ruppel and David Bernstein at McGraw-Hill in New York. Without this serendipitous series of meetings, followed by encouragement and support, this volume for the Americas would not have happened. So the *Business Week* and McGraw-Hill teams also deserve my thanks for creating this window of opportunity.

Collectively, I must also mention my 660-strong research team at BT laboratories, the managers and people in BT the company, all my colleagues in academia, CSC, and my friends on the TTI Vanguard Advisory Board. In one respect or another, they have influenced and directed my thinking and productivity.

Without all these people, this book would not be, and I would not have achieved so much so fast. To all of them, I extend a warm thank you.

"For tribal man
space was the uncontrollable mystery.
For technological man
it is time that occupies the same role"

—Marshall McLuhan, 1951

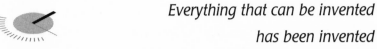

*Everything that can be invented
has been invented*

Charles H. Duell
U.S.Commissioner of Patents (1897)

WHY TIPS FOR TIME TRAVELERS?

My grandfather was once heard to say that man would never fly; my father said we would never get to the moon; and I say to my children that I find it hard to conceive of any single barrier that we will not overcome given sufficient time and technology. After all, we have mastered conventional three dimensional space. We can freely move anywhere anytime, even fly to the moon, and if we had the political will, well beyond.

Our true destiny lies in mastering time itself. I think we can safely assume that no one understands time; it remains one of the greatest mysteries—perhaps the primary one— for our species. As a measured quantity, it slips through our fingers in a unilateral flow, never to be halted, never to be repeated, but at an accelerating rate as we age. None of us has enough time. A continual stream of technology has allowed successive generations to do and realize more than those who went before. For the generations alive today, and those to come, the process is moving into overdrive, and it is in danger of getting away from us.

My job, my life, and my mission is to live in the future, to be a pathfinder, at least five years ahead of any other human, and ten years ahead of most. This role I have occupied for many years, living with, using, and being subject to the latest technology emerging from my laboratory and those we collaborate with worldwide. So it seems to me that in one sense I am a time traveler, since I have to flip between the old, new, and "you haven't seen it yet" worlds of work and play.

Thinking up a title for this volume was, therefore, straightforward, since I have chosen to record many of my experiences, thoughts, and warnings for the future. In reality we are all time travelers, and this book records my tips for those yet to travel the same or similar paths.

Unlike the majority of science fiction writers, I do not anticipate technology leading to some cataclysm or apocalyptic end for humanity and planet earth. History is reassuring on that count. But along with the opportunities for doing good, there are also dangers in a future that will be increasingly dominated by technology. Hopefully, the "tips" recorded here will help prompt the right thoughts and questions and alert all time travelers to what is about to come.

1

*"He had decided
to live forever
or die in the attempt."*

Joseph Heller (1961)

DEATH BY INSTALLMENTS

If you were dying and all your mental faculties were complete, would you consent to the transferring of your mental awareness and capability into a computer? Most people I have asked say categorically no. Now, suppose the transfer was into an android with the ambulatory and tactile qualities of you the real person. The majority of people still say no. But I would say yes to either extreme and everything in between.

I once asked my wife if she would still love me if I had to have a tin leg. She responded with an immediate yes. She remained steadfast at the further prospect of a prosthetic arm, artificial heart, kidneys, pancreas, lungs, spleen, stomach, and inner ear. But when I suggested artificial eyes, she responded with a resounding no, followed by, "Just a minute, I am not having you dying by installments."

The question I then posed was: At what point are you going to say it is not me inhabiting an amalgam of flesh, blood, metal, and electronics? Is it when we make the final step of transferring my biologically developed brain to an electronically manufactured brain?

For the most part, these are questions people do not wish to contemplate. For me they are a rerun of a mind experiment some years after my father died. Had the technology been available to capture his consciousness from his dying body, I think he would have said yes. However, my mother reacted vehemently against the very thought

3

of transferring a loved one into a machine form. Interestingly, I would have done anything to have maintained contact with that intellect, that being who had initiated my life, nurtured, taught, and loved me from the moment I was born until we finally parted. His physical manifestation mattered less to me than his presence. I would have done anything to have maintained contact with him in whatever form. For various reasons, I never had the courage to ask him this question, and I will always wonder which decision he would have made. I suppose as I age this question will be a recurring one and may even become pertinent. If not pertinent for me, then it will certainly be pertinent for my son's son, or whomever. At some point in the future it is almost certain our technology will be able to transfer human minds into a silicon form.

At our present rate of progress, 20 years will see computers with an equivalent processing and storage capability to us, but this is just a start. Within 30 years the development of such machines should have reached our desks or pockets. Whether they will be capable of supporting new life forms, or imbibing existing ones, remains to be seem. Probably the key challenge they will help us solve is the understanding of and access to the human mind itself. We do not understand how the human brain works, since we have not yet unravelled its unbelievable complexity. Perversely, with future super computers, it might be possible for us to create sufficiently good models to achieve a full understanding.

What kind of world will it be, where no one ever has to die, or for that matter suffer unbearable sickness and failure of health? A world where we can live inside a static machine or communications network or inhabit some android or robotic form? The answer: It will be totally different from anything we have experienced. Perhaps life and society will take on new forms—with the merging of intelligence and experience. We may even become civilized and stop slaughtering each other.

2

*"And still they gazed,
and still the wonder grew,
that one small head
could carry all he knew."*

Oliver Goldsmith

A HUMAN HEADFUL

Friday evenings usually see me going home exhausted, with eight hours work set aside for the weekend. But on Saturday morning this work is completed in less than an hour. My head is no longer full; I'm no longer in overload; sleep has restored my energy and abilities. How come I am unable to just work flat out? What is this tiredness that my computer never suffers? It seems to be a combination of raw energy rundown and storage capacity overload. This can be accompanied by mild nausea brought on by a rapidly changing itinerary of people and topics, electronic and paper information I/O. I have reached my limit, and it is principally mental, not physical.

All biological organisms function as information processors; they take in information about their environment, process and use it to locate the necessary energy sources for survival. They are driven, therefore, by disorder (entropy-information) processing. The more efficiently organisms process and extract information from their environment, the more successfully they and their offspring continue their existence. Organisms are perpetuated at the expense of the less efficient—the smartest win. And so it seems to be in business and management.

The last two billion years of life has been driven by carbon-based molecular systems based on a combination of random mutation and natural selection. Homo sapiens arose through this molecular-based Darwinian evolution during the last two million years. And our future evolution depends on understanding that living creatures are information processors, that is, consumers of entropy rather than just energy. This implies that systems that are more efficient at information processing may one day supplant us. Indeed, for task-specific applications this is axiomatic and exemplified by autopilots, engine management systems, and robotic mass production plants. But perhaps the difficulties the world chess champion Kasparov had with Deeper Blue give a better barometer of progress. Only 10 years ago many believed such open-ended games as chess would always be beyond the limitations of computers, but no longer. Given the rate of progress in computer hardware and artificial intelligence, even Deeper Blue will not want to bother playing Kasparov within five years.

It is the ability of an organism, or organization, to process information about its environment that is a driving force behind evolution. If there is evolutionary pressure to evolve better brains to survive, then genetic engineering and other biological options will not help if our brain is inherently limited by architecture and operational modes. The next step in "evolution" would then be to appropriate silicon as the intelligence medium to augment our wetware. Future evolution would then be driven by mechanisms and forces radically different from those manifestly of nature. Further Darwinian evolution could lead to a creeping carbon-silicon mix.

At some point biological systems become inherently limited as they encounter fundamental physical limitations that constrain, direct, or prevent further evolution in some direction. The most obvious examples are the limitations on size imposed on insects by their ability to transport oxygen and the stress limits of bone in land-based mammals, dictating the leg thickness needed to support their weight. For us, it is the limitations to both our frames and brains. Having enjoyed two million years of encephalization, we have hit the end stop. Our brain gets no bigger.

If we as a species are to compete in a machine-dominated culture, where are we going to find the necessary brain capacity? For certain, it will not be through the enhancement of our carbon-based wetware. We only have two choices: internal or external silicon extension.

3

"The press, the machine, the railway, the telegraph are premises whose thousand-year conclusion no one has yet dared to draw."

Friedrich Nietzsche (1880)

CHIPS UNDER THE SKIN

An ever-growing bulge in my jacket pocket recently prompted me to count the stack of plastic cards I now possess. These ranged from credit and bank to security pass, vending, airline, hotel, insurance, health, and retail. They numbered a surprising 27 in all. This further motivated me to investigate my checkbooks, building society, health care, passport, driver's license, insurance, and related documents, which totalled another 23 items. My mind then turned to addresses. Home, office, telephone, e-mail, home page, social security, pension, and the like revealed a further 32 items. Surely this is not a paradigm that can last. Who wants to live this way?

Reflecting on the madness of a world awash with 21st century technology embedded in 16th century processes, the inconvenience of the train ticket, coinage, and rubber stamp mentality also stood out. Consider the inconvenience. From passport control at airports to supermarkets, waiting and standing in line is now endemic. Often the cost of waiting exceeds the cost of goods, or amounts to a substantial proportion of a total journey's total time. Just how much waiting time does a loaf of bread or an apple warrant? What is a reasonable proportion of the total cost? Well, most people get paid more than one apple a minute or a pack of sandwiches an hour. On this basis, buying a house or a car is very efficient. But drive two hours to an international airport, arrive two hours early to check in, fly for nine hours, and then spend over an hour waiting to get into a distant country because someone has to flick through the paper pages of your passport. Having confirmed it is you, your handcrafted customs and immigration declarations are the final barrier to entry. Then, travel an hour to a hotel and spend 15 minutes checking in because they too have to check your details. Travel within country and the proportion of wasted time is even greater because of the shorter flight times. So time in line exceeds goods.

Buying everything from socks to gasoline, it is the same. Information processing by humans is the limiting factor. What should we be doing? Well, a single chip on a smart card can now store all the above information and much more. Our medical records, insurance, passport, bank details, and employment histories could be written into the one device. Add a short-range wireless transmitter-receiver and we have a personal transponder, just like an aircraft. We can be identified and information accessed or updated with no physical connection. So in principle, all our problems are over. Just wander into a store, collect what you want, swipe as you go, and we are the masters of our own delay.

Of course, there are worries about security. Suppose someone stole your card, or you lost it, or worse still, the information on it was accessed electronically. Perhaps a PIN is insufficient protection, and anyway, with this sophistication who wants to keep punching buttons? Perhaps an electronic signet ring would do the trick. One thing for sure, it could not be more insecure than the paper and plastic systems we use today.

Logically, a better scheme would be a chip implant. Just a small slice of silicon under the skin is all it would take for us to enjoy the freedom of no cards, passports, or keys. Put your hand out to the car door, computer terminal, the food you wish to purchase, and you would be instantly recognized and be dealt with efficiently. Think about it—total freedom, no more plastic.

4

"I have experienced public discussions of cloning by religious leaders and it has not been edifying."

Richard Dawkins (1997)

TECHNOLOGY DENIAL SILICONE OR SILICON?

There was a time when we could be educated for life in our first 22 years. For the rest of our existence we could gracefully get out of step with progress and complain increasingly about the changing world as we approached a grumpy death. But not any more, the world is moving too fast, and we have to keep up in an exponential race with technology. Our growing dependence on technology is, and always has been, irreversible. There is no going back without paying a terrible price. Everything we consume is created, organized, and delivered by machines and networks. There are now too many people and not enough rabbits and berries to support the populace; without modern technology most of us would die. How strange then that we live in a society where technological ignorance is so often lauded and even celebrated. But the people who deny technology are not only an impediment to progress and rational decision making, they are a risk to all about them. Invoking superstitious or emotional reactions to apparently complex situations can be both expensive and dangerous. We all have a responsibility to keep on top of change, to keep educated. We can no longer afford to opt out, because there is no escape.

When faced with death, or the prospect of a seriously degraded quality of life, even the most ardent technophobes and antivivisectionists do not refuse an artificial implant. At this point, replacement hearts, lungs, livers, and kidneys res-

9

cued from other humans are no longer an issue or big news. Even piece parts from animals or those created in any artificial or mechanical way are gratefully received, and it makes for emotive headline material. The reality is that despite professed reservations, the immediacy of death prompts the vast majority to opt for life-saving technology, no matter what its origins. It is not too difficult, therefore, to envisage a creeping evolution towards a cyborg world of partially artificial people. It already looks as though some 30 percent of our bodies can be replaced, artificially repaired, or modified to advantage.

If asked to choose between a human or robotic surgeon, a joint of pork or beef, coal or atomic power generation, most would make the wrong decision. Robotic surgeons can achieve orders of magnitude of more precision than any human; eating beef is far less risky than crossing the road; and burning coal does untold damage to us and the planet. People get alarmed at the prospect of silicon implants for humans, but will happily put their names down for silicone implants. On the one hand the material is inert and safe, and on the other there are very definite risks. So our society debates for some ideal physical perfection of form and against the potential to repair damaged human beings. It seems political correctness and ignorance are now more powerful forces in the decision process than logic and understanding.

On the basis of such wisdom we see beneficial research restricted and curtailed, as the new species, homo-Ludditus, emerges with a call to stop progress. This has to be the most dangerous move of all. Do we really want to slide back to the dark ages when fear and mystery of the unknown ruled our lives? Or do we want to understand more so we can make wise decisions? To progress as a species, we need society to be better educated and to have a more symbiotic relationship with technology. It is vital that more people understand the fundamentals. Not to do so will see us relegated to a second rate and disabled species.

5

"The agent . . . .
just takes ten percent
of your life."
Raymond Chandler (1952)

AGENTS GOOD AND BAD

In our real world we have become conditioned to all manner of agents. Examples include insurance and banking, police and state, sellers of property, company, security, and, of course, the secret agent. There are also rafts of abstract and less visible agents at work in chemical processes, medicine, biology, cookery, farming, and much more. In almost every case these agents have beneficial properties and are used for good. Occasionally, the temptation to become more efficient at killing and maiming prompts us to create defoliants and other agents of damage and death. So we cannot assume all agents are good; they are not, but mostly because we are the controlling agent.

Recent developments in our electronic world have seen much excitement among those working on software agents. In this virtual world we look forward to new forms of agent that will search out information, manage vast networks of technology, and organize our daily lives. Their intelligence can be expected to progress to the point that they will be able to negotiate IT services, software application upgrades, and modifications. In a relatively short time we may see them scheduling journeys, buying and selling commodities, and relieving us of a considerable amount of mundane work.

Managing complex systems, resources, and workloads should be the forte of agent technologies. They are born of an era of chaos, and they are ideally suited to deal with it. To date, we see modest levels of agent intelligence doing increasingly complex tasks well beyond the established routes created by conventional software. Experiments are also underway to create systems that allow agents to breed, taking advantage of the best attributes created through a continual genetic exchange and chance mutation. Such technology should, in theory, be capable of keeping up with us as we adapt and adopt new technologies and working practices.

Now the obvious question arises: Will all electronic agents be good? This seems unlikely, looking at our past history of bending good technology to malicious purpose. Someone is bound to create bad agents—spies and wreckers of systems. In fact, anything we have already done in the physical world is likely to be emulated and exceeded. Someone, some organization or group, is just bound to seize this opportunity to bomb, extort, and manipulate this technology to advantage. But is there more?

For the first time the agents we deal with will have the ability to mutate and develop beyond human imagination. They may assume the proportions of medieval diseases to disfunctionalize individuals, organizations, and society. Their evolutionary rate will exceed that of biological systems, and their host will be every computer and network on the planet. Every disc and chip will be a potential hiding place and incubator.

Should we be panicking or trying to stop these developments now? Probably not. For one, this technology is such a power for good, and for another, it is unstoppable. Someone somewhere will do it anyway. We have to be first, build and understand all its facets before the hands of evil have a chance to make a move.

We have the ability to create good agents that can combat the bad. A very fast conversation at their first meeting will reveal the purpose and intent. Good can compare notes and learn from each other as can the bad. But the overwhelming balance has to be good, just like our human society. It is a necessary condition; otherwise the system would collapse. A network immune system, complete with white agents (cells), could combat almost any attack provided it is big enough to surround and smother the offending entities.

6

BANKING ON IT

For eons we have taken raw materials and shaped them into artifacts we could barter. Physical articles have been dominant in the marketplace, with money the vital lubricant of commerce. Now we face a new and ethereal market, a world of bits, not raw material. While manufacturing bits can be very expensive, their replication, storage, transportation, and selling are not. Here computers, networks, and terminals replace warehouses, trucks, wholesalers, and shops to distribute faster and sell far more.

Macroeconomies based on microprices are becoming significant as more software and services are sold on CD or on-line. Classic books, reference works, and interactive multimedia entertainment packages are available; more than 25,000 CD titles are now on sale for a few dollars. The complete works of William Shakespeare cost only 3 cents on a CD along with 2000 other works. Many soft products can also be purchased on-line direct from manufacturers worldwide. Even travel services, furniture, clothing, and food are available on-line. This is creating a future of micromoney and macroeconomies. The new on-line companies will see some remarkable new phenomenon, as people buy and discard products faster, markets become more fickle, and competition more transient. In this new world companies are likely to be created, come to dominate, and then die faster, as the economic cycle also speeds up.

These new industries will require new forms of commerce—new ways to charge and pay—in a far faster world of much more for much less.

Banks will have to become electronic databases with no human intervention. Checks and coinage are uneconomic for such small transactions. It is also clear that anyone with a PC and a modest programming capability could open their own bank. Car manufacturers and telephone operating companies have already moved into banking and financial services. Perhaps software suppliers will do the same and make enormous savings by becoming distributor, wholesaler, retailer, *and* banker. One computer company recently put its sales and marketing catalog on-line and now deals with 1.7 million inquiries a week.

All of this will erode the traditional banking sector and will be compounded by a disappearing commodity, coinage. It seems remarkable that metallic and paper tokens (money) are still used in a world of information technology and electronics. Credit cards, electronic cash cards, and the electronic purse are already in everyday use. In this information world, no money is exchanged; databases are merely updated. There is no gold or any need for it. It is a moribund concept. In a sense, geography is also dead, and for the customer the choice will become increasingly stark. You can still travel into town, with all the inconvenience and time-wasting it entails, and pay the additional overhead of a shop, wholesaler, and distribution chain. Alternatively, you can go direct to a manufacturer, even overseas, make a purchase and have your software delivered on-line at a fraction of the price, bypassing VAT in two countries. At the same time the databases of only two banks, customer and producer, change negligibly—no one in the middle, no non-value-add links in the chain.

We can now see banking as just information transactions. In 20 years we may look back with wry humor at those who currently argue for regional currencies bearing the profile of the head of state. Such concepts are likely to have been assigned to museums as the obvious alternative, bits, takes over. The world economy is being transformed by IT, and by 2015 some coinage and paper money might remain, and perhaps even a few checks, but I'd bank on IT.

7

"The habit of common and continuous speech is a symptom of mental deficiency. It proceeds from not knowing what is going on in other people's minds."

Walter Bagehot (1878)

MACHINE TALK

Communication—information processing and storage—on planet earth is now dominated by the digital computer. So it might seem curious to imagine computers conversing with each other through spoken English instead of their natural binary mode. How slow it would be, apparently pointless and potentially frustrating. After all, digital communication is millions of times faster and more precise than any analogue human tongue. And yet in a recent experiment a text-to-speech system successfully interacted with a speech-to-text converter. Both were PC-based with a humanized voice and adaptive digital speech recognition. The remarkable outcome of this experiment was the apparent ease with which these machines could communicate without error. They seemed at least as good as some human subjects, and even in a noisy room they coped well. Most surprising of all, they could also converse over a standard telephone line. In fact, the more they practiced the better they rapidly became, even more so than human subjects.

Could it be that digital machines are so invariant, their utterances so absolute, prescriptive, and precise, that they are superior to our own? For us, every analogue utterance of the same sentence, word, or sound is subtly different, and to make things worse, we use this variability to convey emotion and meaning. This is further complicated by the fact that we often do not say what we mean, or mean what we say. We also have a habit of creating a wide range of words and sentences that mean the same, or very similar. In contrast, machines employ and tolerate far less redundancy. Our variability is a major limiter to concise and accurate communication between ourselves, and worse, with machines. On the other hand it is also a mark of our extraordinary abilities and richness of culture. We are definitely subtle communicators and in many respects well ahead of machines—for now.

So here comes a new and exciting paradigm, with humankind and machine ultimately conversing on an apparently common level. Today we can only do simple things like find a telephone number or purchase goods. But it is a start, and voice interaction with machines will gradually become commonplace, giving rise to new environments, services, applications, and problem sets.

We may only be a short way off voice command and interaction with all electrical appliances as a dominant mode over the button, knob, keyboard, and mouse. Talking to your car, television, radio, home, and computer is all increasingly possible. Voice announcements, messaging, e-mail, text to speech, and speech to text are already with us in trial services and some commercial products. Their great advantage is that we can choose and adapt the communication mode to meet our individual skills and requirements. Driving a car while using a mobile phone, navigator, or computer is difficult, dangerous, and illegal. However, talking to such devices is easy and safe.

Several machines joining groups of humans in conversation may seem a strange concept today, but once we can converse with them, it will happen. I will bring my semisentient machine to meetings with me, and so will others. So when two or more machines are present, will they talk in a human tongue or binary? For our sake it has to be a human tongue, at least during the period when we need to be in the loop of knowing. Interestingly, there will be a new silico-duplicity as the machines converse behind our backs, invisibly shifting MBytes, negotiating, arranging, and dealing to our mutual benefit. But their biggest contribution may be to refine our language and improve our accuracy and efficiency.

8

*"It takes a long time
to become young."*

Pablo Picasso

5 OR 50

In a recent experiment I laid out 10 top-end computers at a gathering of senior managers. The majority just looked on, and only a few plucked up courage to sit down and play. But to a man and woman they all reacted in the same way. They sat down and asked, "What do I do?" Interestingly, the same experiment with 5-year-old children did not invoke the same response. None of the children would just watch; they all wanted hands-on, and none asked, "What do I do?" They just did.

Having studied this phenomenon further, I discovered an interesting statistic. If you are 10 years old or less, the chances are you have had at least the same amount of computer flying hours as someone who is 50 or more. At 5 and below you have no fear, because in part, you have not paid for the machine, and the thought of breaking it does not pose a threat. It is even unlikely to be a conscious thought. If you are 50 or above and you have purchased the machine, you come with a mindset that says a $2000 expenditure is serious folding money and I'd better be careful I don't damage the machine. You are automatically inhibited and in many cases somewhat overawed by the technology itself. You reach for the handbook. Children seldom use handbooks. They live in a "crash and burn" world of trial and error, and more reassuringly, talking to their peer group, exchanging ideas and experience, learning by doing.

It is also interesting to reflect that if you are 50 years old, you are more likely to be extremely busy, finding it difficult to sit down and familiarize yourself with technology and simply play. Moreover, you are fast running out of lifetime years to do this effectively. In contrast, at 10 years old you come equipped with a mindset that assumes you will dominate the technology. You also have an abundance of spare time and lifetime years in which to familiarize yourself and become competent. In short, 50-year-olds will never be able to keep up with the 10-year-olds; they will be overtaken. We now have the situation where the generation gap is manifest in a 40 year lack of experience. So the people with the technological understanding and capability find decisions imposed upon them by people 40 years older with only a fraction of the capability.

Exposure to computers and related technologies is occurring at an earlier and earlier stage of life. The simplest teaching machines can now be bought for a few bucks, and include voice synthesis, simple pictures, and a good deal of interactivity. For many children the education and experience build-up for the information world starts before they are one year old. It is acquired in the same way that we learn to throw, write, walk, and eat. It is not an adjunct, something special, or something that is taught as a subject. It is subsumed like language and becomes completely intuitive. It is surprising then that these children at the age of 5 are feeling very comfortable with the technology and by the age of 10 are undeniably skilled and capable people. What chance then the 50-year-old? Who knows? Perhaps we will be able to look forward to a sunset period of our lives where responsibility is subsumed earlier down the age structure so that we can have time to play too. One thing for sure, we will see more 5-year-old consultants.

9

*"There is no reason
for any individual
to have a computer
in their home."*

Ken Olsen, President, DEC (1977)

NEW AGE NOMADS

Twenty years ago we were all getting very excited at the prospect of the paperless office. What happened? We now use more paper than ever before, and for many it still seems something of a dream. Relatively speaking, only a few organizations can claim to have totally changed the way they work and to have become so embedded in IT that paper is now hardly ever used. But in reality far more work and information are now processed and stored by computers than on paper.

The principal mistake made over the past decades was to take the paradigm of the paper-based office and put it directly onto the screen—and then back it all up with paper copies. Computer screens invoke, and allow, a different way of working, a new mode of operation that can now be seen as an entirely different environment. So after 20 years of exploration and wandering in the wilderness, the paperless office starts to arrive—today. Companies and individuals are now moving hard onto the screen, working and networking, and most important, reengineering organizations. The result is a rapid streamlining in operations and management that is fundamentally impossible with paper.

So what of telecommunications? Is there a parallel situation evolving? The telephone, fax machine, mobile phone, television, radio, and more recently, video-conferencing might encourage us to suppose that physical travel will soon be a thing of the past. The reality is that telecommunications is doing for the travel industry what the computer did for the paperless office. We still insist on traveling and meeting people because, the truth is, telecommunications is only a partial solution. In fact telecommunications promotes a desire and need to travel for that vital human contact we find so necessary and enjoy. A more recent merging of technology is promoting this world of travel through the combining of computing and communication with laptop computers, modems, and fixed-line and digital mobile phones. We can now be on-line from the car, train, hotel bedroom, and we see new age nomads everywhere. They travel with suitcase and laptop, connectors, batteries, and modems. For these people the office is where they are; they communicate regardless of location and distance. Their working style is a far cry from the office worker of just five years ago. Indeed, many have no office, and at best, "hot desk" in a number of locations.

Along with such flexibility and the advantage of always being on the move, there is a downside. The divisions between working, playing, home, and office are removed. The world becomes a less divided and a far more fuzzy place. Work never stops, home life is no longer sacrosanct. But on the upside, those sudden bursts of inspiration and desire to do things can be reconciled immediately. You can work when you are most able, most enthusiastic, best motivated. If managed well, it also allows for a greater degree of effective human interaction. During the past decade my work output has gone up tenfold through this advance in technology and new mode of working.

The artificial nature of the telephone and teleconferencing will dictate that we continue to travel more than we should or need for at least another decade. Beyond that, however, technology will be able to deliver such realism that travel will become anathema. And it is vital that this should be the case. Otherwise, we stand to not only destroy countries but the whole of the human environment. Burning hydrocarbons at an accelerating rate is untenable but burning bits is no problem.

10

"Physicists use the wave theory on Mondays, Wednesdays and Fridays, and the particle theory on Tuesdays, Thursdays and Saturdays."

Sir William Henry Bragg

INFORMATION WAVES

Anyone who drives on major highways will have experienced traffic waves created by some unseen event ahead. A good place to experience this phenomenon is on the New York's Belt Parkway where, for no apparent reason, speeds can oscillate between 10 and 70 mph for long periods. Sometimes the traffic comes to a complete halt and then lurches forward to 40 mph and back down to 0. This is the classic behavior of a system of independent entities in a serial queue having a delay between observation and action. In this case the observation might be an accident, a breakdown, or someone driving foolishly. The delay is between the eye, brain, and foot. As soon as we see something and touch the brake pedal, then very shortly afterwards so does everyone else, and so the wave starts.

There is no doubt about it; rubbernecking when driving a car is very dangerous, but people do it. An accident or incident occurs and people slow down to take a look, and then on the far side they speed up. Strangely, when the incident has been cleared away, the wave that has been set in motion may last the rest of the day. If the traffic is dense, the wave motion persists long after the event has subsided. The system has an unseen memory—us. Might we then expect similar phenomena in electronic systems for communication between people and machines? This is a racing certainty and the technology and phenomenon is already with us.

Packet switching and transmission systems so beloved of the computer industry are ideal for the creation of information waves. To date, these have largely gone unnoticed because terminal equipment's assemble packets to construct a complete message, file, or picture. The end user sees nothing of the chaotic action inside the network as the information packets jostle for position and queue for transmission. Only when we try to use computer networks for real-time communication do we experience any arrival uncertainties. Our speech sounds strange, with varying delays in the middle of utterances, and moving pictures contain all manner of distortion and deviation from the truth.

The reality is that packet systems are fundamentally unsuited to real-time communication between people and machines. So why use them? It turns out that for data communication where arrival time is not an issue, they are highly efficient in their use of bandwidth. These systems were born in an era where bandwidth was expensive, and they represent an entirely different paradigm for switching and transmission compared to the telephone network. However, the champions of "packet everything" always like to tell you that this is the true way for information to be communicated. Curiously, they often do this by sending you a single line e-mail message with a 35-line header.

So what of the future? We now have a world of optical fiber and infinite bandwidth, a world of shrinking geography, where distance is becoming irrelevant and where the fundamental reliability of networks, communication, and computing is increasingly dependent upon the electronics used for transmission and switching. If we are to see significant advances in reliability and performance, then the eradication of much of the electronics used today has to be inevitable. The contest will then be between two philosophies, the circuit switching of the telephone network and the path or packet switching of the computer industry. But because an optical fiber is like the Belt Parkway, with a million lanes and no bad drivers, it might just be that these two diverse approaches will coalesce with the switching of light.

11

And he that will this health deny.
Down among the dead men let him die.

John Dyer (1714)

TELE-HEALTH

Early in the new century, the number of people needing some form of daily care and support will more than double, while the number of potential carers will fall by a factor of at least three. At the same time the numbers gainfully employed in creating wealth will halve, and those capable of becoming professionals will also fall as a percentage of the total population. Undoubtedly, we will also see people failing to provide adequately for an extended old age and their siblings refusing to pick up the tab. How, then, are a diminishing band of carers going to cope with a growing customer expectation and demand, when resources and funding will at best remain static, and most likely will fall?

No doubt, clinicians and carers will continue to refine their techniques and become ever more efficient, while administrators shave out costs, reduce bed occupancy, and get patients back into the community ever faster. But none of this will be enough to stem the tide of demand and the growing inability to respond. Something new is required to change the care paradigm, which has fundamentally been in stasis for over a century.

At present we see something of a dichotomy: while industry delayers reduces the number of managers and embraces IT and change, healthcare seems to go in the opposite direction. The height of this absurdity has been reached in some hospitals where each patient now has a dedicated administrator. Also, consider patient records, with the GP, nurse, specialist, consultant, radiologist, and anaesthetist gathering the same basic information during just one illness. This is often repeated for successive illnesses and/or visits. The biggest single innovation in patient records during the last century has been to redesign the cart in which the paper is carried.

Patients travel to hospitals; doctors, nurses, and specialists travel to patients and hospital. With head- and hand-mounted cameras, VR headsets and videoconferencing, it is now possible to effect remote diagnosis, A&E support of paramedics at an accident site, dermatological examinations, fetal scanning, endoscopy, and operations of all kinds without expensive physical travel.

At a more basic level, consider the nurse who gives up her handbag for a laptop computer, digital camera, and mobile phone. At the push of a few keys the abilities of a GP can be extended to some remote location and an image of a wound or infection captured on screen and transmitted back to the remote surgery. Pictorial records of progress can be archived for later comparison and use, while reassuring consultancy is always at hand.

Beyond the demands for medical care, we will see a rise in loneliness and need for verbal and visual support. Everyone has TV, radio, and telephone, and many have camcorders and PCs. The technology for videoconferencing is now fundamentally inexpensive and available. Support communities on the Internet already exist for just about any disease or condition imaginable. Thousands of people worldwide communicate and compare notes, offering advice and experience beyond that available via traditional routes. Extending this facility to everyone is potentially inexpensive; WWW-TV set-top-box systems roll out at about the price as a SatCom terminal.

Of course, there are threats and risks. Smart patients will use IT to get ahead of the professionals. By being better informed they can ask more perceptive questions, demand treatments, and be more demanding customers. But perhaps worse still, countries will export their medical services to compete in other markets. The Internet already makes it possible to bypass restrictions on the drugs and medicines available over the counter, and soon it may be diagnosis and treatment that is on immediate offer.

12

"Information networks straddle the world. Nothing remains concealed. But the sheer volume of information dissolves the information. We are unable to take it all in."

Günther Grass (1990)

SERENDIPITY DO WE HAVE A CHOICE ?

The medieval librarian was the guardian and regulator of information, the contents list, index, filing system, and retrieval mechanism. He alone decided who saw what, when, and where. There was no open information access; it was strictly regulated and controlled. So what chance serendipity? Not much. For over 200 years we have enjoyed increasing levels of serendipity with the decimalization of paper libraries and the librarian's transition from guardian to assistant and information agent. Through this openness we see a high degree of serendipity by merely walking through rows of shelves and chance spotting that book or obscure journal. Even daily newspapers afford a high degree of serendipity through the mechanisms of headline and picture.

Contrast all of this with the seemingly infinite world of the Internet. Here we have almost 100 percent serendipity, an abundance of data with an overriding lack of order, no signposts or eye-catching indicators. Actually finding what you want is now a challenge. Being totally awash with serendipity poses a new problem. In this environment, information seems to come in two dominant classes: that which is of no interest and that which is distracting, interesting, but still of no direct benefit. The problem is now to find anything that you actually require.

Poles apart from the Internet, we have the CD ROM, with almost zero serendipity. So well organized, sterile, and deep is this medium that drilling down to the information you require can involve over five clicks of a mouse. A total lack of visibility of information on either side of the mine shaft you dig is also a limiter. You can soon find yourself totally lost and disoriented, with no frame of reference to help, so you resort to Control Quit and start again.

Perhaps somewhere between the Internet and CD ROM lies the ideal world, with the right percentage of serendipity that allows us to optimize our creativity and rate of work. The question is how it is to be realized. Serendipity by design is a major challenge, for in the past we have created such worlds by accident. Perhaps we have to wait for the electronic evolution to spontaneously create this serendipitous environment for us. But I suspect not. For while the world of electronic information is on a scale so colossal it defeats the human mind to contemplate its vastness, we have already experienced the delights of serendipity, and we have some measure of its value to us. Intuitively, we feel we should be able to manufacture it.

Perhaps we will have to look to artificial agents, who will learn about our habits and interests through direct observation. They could then take on the role of a personal librarian roaming global data banks on our behalf. Perhaps we will have to spend more time with other people discussing our problems and formulating our views to create new forms of serendipity that have so far escaped us. Either way, we face a major challenge, since mankind's knowledge base is now doubling in a period of less than 2 years. This is especially so with the creation of increasing levels of short-term information that just acts as a fog to us when spotting what we are really looking for. We are going to need help through increasing levels of computing power and artificial intelligence. There are no human attributes that will enable us to cope with the massively increased levels of serendipity we now have and will increasingly see. We have to hope that the machines can help us, or face an increasingly sterile and less creative world.

13

"If there is technological advance
without social advance, there is,
almost automatically, an increase
in human misery, in impoverishment."
Michael Harrington (1962)

HAVES AND HAVE NOTS

Quite rightly, there is deep concern in many sectors that our society is increasingly becoming divided by the information haves and have nots. The common perception is that this division is a function of financial wealth. The reality is that the division appears to be strongly weighted by age. Roughly speaking, at 29 years old and above, people are computer illiterate, while below this age the chances are they have a degree of computer literacy. Although this is a gross generalization, it does point to a critical division by age and technophobia. Today, our children are born into a world of IT and first encounters with electronic devices come usually in their first year. At the other end of the spectrum we have in our population many who can remember the time before the invention and arrival of the transistor or integrated circuit. They perceive the technology to be complex, unfriendly, and expensive in terms of money and time.

If we are to combat the dangers of an information division in our society, then availability and easy access are vital. Left to its own devices, the industry will probably continue to produce PCs of ever-increasing capability at more or less a constant price. Competition from the brown goods sector may soon change this. The first integrated television and personal computer units have been announced at a price little more than a top-end TV. There are also numerous trials on cable and satellite systems using intelligent set-top boxes to provide access to information services and the

Internet. But perhaps the most exciting future possibility is the development of systems such as Java and low-cost computer terminal and network computing.

Whatever the choice and opportunity provided by technology, the biggest hurdle to success is, by far, technophobia, and it is age-related. The easiest way of breaking down this fear is to get on a machine and succumb to the assistance of an available child. Children come from a world of crash and burn, of experimentation and no handbooks. They consult, confer, and learn very fast. They also delight in helping others, regardless of age. For them the computer screen is a natural place to be, and not a place to be feared.

For those who argue that the disadvantaged are dominated by those facing a financially challenging world, it is interesting to assess the true distribution of wealth. Looking at this problem in terms of the number of television sets, VHS recorders, hi-fi systems, and games machines in the average home, along with the money invested in transportation and designer label and luxury clothing, we gain a different picture. It really is a question of how much people value the technology and how useful it is to them that dictates investment patterns and access to the information world. Once people discover the usefulness and powerful nature of this new paradigm, then money is quickly directed into purchasing equipment and software.

One challenge that hits rich and poor alike in this IT world is to keep up-to-date, for within three years a top end product will become out moded and start to look lame. However, that does not preclude their use in education and training in the broad sense. It does not make them totally useless—just limited.

Then, of course, there is the issue of the cost of communication and connection. When it comes to getting on-line and cruising the Internet, it is interesting to compare the cost to that of purchasing or renting videos, running a car, buying a pint of beer, or the purchase of a very few other luxury goods. None of this technology is really all that expensive.

14

POLITICALLY CORRECT BRAINS

In just over 2,000,000 years we have become *numero uno* in the intelligence stakes, but our wetware looks to have reached its evolutionary peak. Weighing in at around 1 kg, the human brain is about 10 cm in diameter, contains some 10,000,000,000 neurons, and a connectivity of around 10,000 per neuron. In our recent past Neanderthal man had a brain 15 to 20 percent larger and the potential to be smarter. But a number of key factors appear to have precluded this possibility. First was the inability to remove heat without the cooling (vascular) systems dominating the brain space (we generate about the same heat output as a 50 watt light bulb in a 10 cm cavity). Second, the signal transmission span and synaptic speed are dictated by reaction times essential to avoid physical threats and danger. There are also limiting trade-offs between the size of the vascular system and the density, capacity, and synaptic interconnection. Intelligence depends on rapid and massive signal processing of pulses at the synapses. In computer terms the pulse width is linked to the clock speed, and processing cannot occur faster than a single clock cycle. If pulses cannot be made shorter, then they dictate the maximum processing speed.

For our metabolism to support a bigger brain would mean more blood flow, faster food-to-energy conversion, and a stronger neck. A much larger brain would need more damping for shock absorption when accelerating and decelerating. With a 1 m diameter head, we would be in danger of suffering a concussion every time we started or stopped walking as our brains crashed into the inside of our skulls.

When the combination of processing time at synapses, transmission speed along axons, and neural density are considered, then the connectivity we now enjoy appears near optimal for processing performance. However, as a model, it does not appear to be a definitive guide for designing other systems, a prerequisite of an intelligent system, or an overall limit. Whales and dolphins have larger brains, but they have large portions specialized for SONAR processing and communication over long distances. They also enjoy a larger vascular system and heat benign environment.

While the measurable differences in size, and perhaps structure, of male and female brains have become a high point of political correctness, it may have a basis in purpose and role. Size/intelligence estimates show little difference and may even favor the smaller brain because of its marginally better packing density and connectivity. But this difference looks to be related to the need to accurately throw projectiles with thousands of our neurons acting in parallel to overcome their individual noisy nature. Unlike silicon brains, ours deal in uncertainty, with the biological neurons constructed from about 1000 individual cells. Such a small number of base elements makes them essentially noisy—in some respects, quantum devices. In stark contrast we design transistorized logic to switch with great precision. One world is full of life, emotion, and intelligence; the other is cold, deterministic, and dead. This realization has recently seen the engineering of noisy neural networks purposely arranged not to be deterministic.

So what separates us and our noisy neurons from those in the latest machines? Only scale and sensors. Our awareness comes from sight, sound, touch, smell, and taste. We can now give all of this to a machine in a form that could be superior to ours. They could have experience over a far wider spectrum than us and also have additional abilities. It would thus seem that the only limiter is scale. Given the present rate of progress, the year 2015 may see us equalled. What price political correctness when we have man, woman, and machine? It might just be that machine born of man will be smartest of all.

15

"All animals are equal
but some animals are
more equal than others."

George Orwell (1945)

ARE ALL BITS REALLY EQUAL?

It's not unusual to hear pundits declare that a bit is a bit is a bit. The philosophically held belief is that "all bits are made equal in the eyes of man and machine." Well, even the Romans (Petronius Arbiter, circa 60AD) figured out that the most important message was the least expected one, and thus all bits are not equal. So, is a telephone bit really the same value as a TV bit? Sometimes this is undoubtedly the case, but a fire alarm or burglar alarm bit really is worth knowing about. And the bit that says your pacemaker is about to fail has even more value. We also require that the validity and security of a TV bit be a vastly different proposition from a bank account or aircraft control system bit. Whatever machines may do or think, it is clear that all bits are not of equal importance or value in the eyes of humankind.

Looking to the telephone network and the Internet, we generally see no costing or classification of bits by worth. From a transport perspective all bits and messages are treated the same. Historically, telephone bits have been seen as expensive, and to date remain dominated by distance, speed, and hold time-related charges. However, the trend is toward reducing infrastructure costs and toward decoupling cost and distance traveled. On the net the illusion has been that bits are free, which they are not. Someone has to pay. The rise of pay-per-click advertising, commercial services, and bit

31

prioritization between real- and delayed-time applications will rapidly kill the illusion of total freedom and bit equality.

In a parallel universe of bit delivery, cable, satellite, and terrestrial TV networks totally ignore distance and supply everything in real time. The considerable expense of doing this is funded by advertising and overdelivery of huge quantities of junk bits. However, the principal money earners are the emotional bits—the emotion conveyed by chat shows, news, sports, and blockbuster movies. It also includes the emotional engagement and demand of the viewers who feel they must witness that sporting event right now. If pay per view is emotionally driven, then perhaps this is also true of the allocation of advertising revenues and license fees that support terrestrial TV. Viewer ratings are emotionally driven; why else do people watch the programs? Of course, it could be plain habit or addiction, but either way any assumption that all bits are equal seems tenuous.

In an interactive world of multimedia the opportunity to charge by bit type, distance, speed, and usage is with us, but it's extremely difficult to tap. In today's telephone networks billing operations are becoming huge and unwieldy, consuming vast resources, and tending toward the uneconomic. The same is true of satellite and cable operations that venture far beyond rental and simple encryption card purchase. In the information world the problem may become really acute, since the number of vendors potentially includes all of us. We can be both consumers and suppliers.

In macroeconomies based on microprices, you cannot pay 20 cents, 2 cents, or 0.2 cents for individual items with a check or a credit card. The processing cost of billing for the exchange of goods for such small amounts of money swamps the per item cost. It is already clear that some businesses can no longer collect their charges economically, and as costs fall further, they could go out of business. So it might just be that in a commerce of bits, the complexity of differentiating between bits and collecting the money might, by default, ultimately render all bits equal.

16

"Information is the oxygen of the modern age. It seeps through the walls topped by barbed wire, it wafts across the electrified borders."

Ronald Reagan (1989)

12 DAYS TO 12 HOURS

My early career was dominated by paper, usually in triplicate, with processing times between groups stretching out to 12 or more days. Drafting a letter, having it typed, corrected, and signed off could take 2 or 3 days. Internal and external mail systems would add another 2 days or more. A letter drafted on a Monday morning would be posted late on Friday, arrive the following Monday, and then the process began again in reverse. Often, a single copy of the correspondence was circulated to several people before a reply was written, with each person adding to the processing time. So all in all, a 12-day turnaround was seen as very respectable.

Today, such delays are intolerable, and the use of fax, telephone, and e-mail have drastically reduced the amount of surface mail as processes speed up. Typing pools and many secretaries have disappeared as more managers have become IT literate. So it is worth asking: What is the ultimate response time?

I live in a 100 percent electronic environment, induced by returning or destroying all internally generated snailmail that could have been sent electronically. But I also promise to respond to all electronic communications within 12 hours. This is a 24 hour per day, 365 day per year obligation on my part. To date my average response time to any e-mail message is 3 hours, with 99 percent answered within 12 hours. So what about the 1 percent? It is inevitable that during some periods of travel on long international flights, or for reasons of family commitments, the 12 hour rule will be occasionally violated.

33

Until recently, I faced a real challenge—the lack of sockets. No phone, hotel room, nor office was safe; I was always hunting for sockets. As soon as I entered a building, I would plug in, log-on, drop my processed mail, then pick up the next batch. While on the face of it this might seem an easy operation, and one that would not cause a technologist too much difficulty, the number of different types of sockets, system delays, and other variables that induce pain are almost infinite. For example, the same RGII telephone connector is used in Europe and the U.S., but unfortunately, the wires are inconveniently shifted over by one pin. So, very often, you can't just plug in. Even now, I go everywhere armed with screwdrivers, alligator clips, and a selection of connectors. This inconvenience is compounded by an incredible variety of dial tones and digital and analogue transmission systems that introduce a variety of signal echoes and distortion. Even a hotel room with three telephones can cause significant difficulties, especially if you don't spot the telephone in the bathroom that may have to be unplugged.

But now there is the digital mobile phone. What an advance. Now I can live a near socket-free life—on-line from car, train, hotel, and restaurant. I can roam across Europe without worry (apart from France, of course, where the dial codes have to be different) and always be on-line. Unfortunately, the system standards and coverage are totally different within Europe and North America. Also, geographical coverage is not 100 percent, so total mobility is not quite possible. Those long Atlantic flights also contribute to my 1 percent failure; although there is a shaver point in the bathroom, there is no phone socket. But I travel 200,000 miles a year, so you may be able to do better than I do. For my foreseeable future it looks as though the socket hunt will continue. So save a place for screwdrivers and crocodile clips.

17

"A man must rise above the earth
to the top of the atmosphere and beyond,
for only then will he fully understand
the world in which he lives."

Socrates (circa 399 BC)

VR—JUST IN TIME

Managing a modern company can be like flying an airliner with more instrumentation than is actually necessary. You can see the temperature of the coffee cups, but your altitude and heading is anybody's guess. You are data rich and information poor, and VR has a big and largely unrecognized part to play. It is ideally suited to the representation of highly complex and data rich situations. Visualizing the operational information of a company is far more edifying than a spreadsheet.

We are very pictographic animals, able to absorb animated, 3D color images at a phenomenal rate. It is unnatural for us to read and write or interpret spreadsheets. We are soon overloaded by information in such formats. Moreover, many of our species have a natural inability to mentally translate 2D drawings (plans) into a 3D world (models). And yet, if information is presented in a natural 3D form, we are all inherently able to absorb and understand the equivalent of a 20-volume encyclopedia in about 15 seconds.

Designing all but the simplest modern products and artifacts on paper has now had its day. Moving to VR affords greater clarity and understanding, facilitates simulation and testing, and as a result, offers great savings. The need to drastically shorten time to market and get products right the first time has brought this technology to the fore. Producing anything from a mobile phone to an airline passenger terminal can see savings of more than 30 percent in time and money through the use of VR. Visualizing the final design in full (virtual) operation is a vital step in getting it right, but without the expense of an actual build.

Medical applications are developing rapidly, with everything from body fly-throughs to operation simulations and animations. In this area, along with many others, it is the mixing of the real and virtual worlds where the greatest advantage probably lies. Combining telepresence and VR allows surgeons the benefit of a real-world view augmented by computer generated simulations. In recent trials surgeons have been able to stand "one inside the other" at a distance to experience new surgical techniques for the first time, or receive reassurance during a first time solo operation. This technology is equally applicable to the repair of a computer, oil refinery, jet engine, or heating plant. It offers a new and alternative approach to education—a metaphoric guide on the inside.

VR also offers significant potential for teaching science, mathematics, and many other topics. It is principally a medium for direct experience, and we can now step inside the atom or the molecule, fly a proton, and experience fission, rather than just gaze at a set of complex equations. We can also dissect a virtual frog and operate a virtual microscope. For the first time, we can see and feel the binding energies in the alignment process of a long chain molecule, while simultaneously viewing the equations and associated graphical information. For many well-understood systems we can already view and handle mathematical functions and models in a new way. They no longer have to be artificially frozen in time and space by the limitation of paper, but can be alive with n-dimensional interactivity.

It is interesting to reflect that only 50 years ago, classes at schools and universities were commonly augmented by practical demonstrations on a laboratory bench that may still be in the front row today. Effectively, that was VR 50 years ago; you just sat and watched someone else do it. Today, much more can be done on the screen by everyone. It may be the tool we have been looking for—instant education and understanding—just in time.

18

"The unpredictability inherent in human affairs is due largely to the fact that the by-products of a human process are more fateful than the product."

Eric Hoffer (1973)

GOODBYE MR. ERLANG

Because telephone customers only make a few short duration calls at random times each day, they only require access to a small fraction of the total switching and network fabric. A residential line might typically see three calls of three minutes per day, made at more or less random times, where as business lines may see over 20 of slightly longer duration. The resource sharing increases beyond the local switch, as traffic is concentrated into a hierarchical global network, and only in the local loop do we all need a dedicated connection. This analysis was characterized by A. K. Erlang, a Danish telephone pioneer working around 1917, and has become holy writ, involving negative exponential distributions and queuing theory. Simply put, as the number of users grows, the more resource aggregation is possible, and the longer you are on the phone, the more likely you are to terminate. Historically, two-hour calls are rare.

Some years ago, a discussion with a computer network team brought home to me just how much the telephone network might have to change. Computer users had complained about the lack of bandwidth and latency, while measurements had established the LAN (local area network) loading to be 25 percent. After some probing, this figure turned out to be the average over a full day. It was then discovered that the average loading for one-hour periods could exceed 55 percent, and 10-minute periods returned 95 percent. The real shock came when the 1-minute figure revealed loadings in excess of 300 percent. Here was the problem, a now obvious oversight, a massive peak-to-mean ratio never experienced in telephone networks.

This problem has since become much worse with the emergence of the Internet. Highly correlated network activities have seen the peak-to-mean ratio increase rapidly to create the World Wide Wait. While the bit transport problem can be solved by providing more bandwidth, a more holistic approach might be to examine network protocols and topologies. We might then simultaneously relieve the strain on routers, switches, and servers.

A growing problem for telephone networks is the hold times associated with net access from fixed and mobile terminals. Instead of three minutes, the average can now be hours, or in the case of polling systems, less than a minute. The Erlang model fails under these extremes because the underlying assumptions are wrong, and resource sharing on a grand scale breaks down.

Large numbers of people making very long telephone calls to a local server rapidly clog up the switching fabric for normal users. This also results in the balance of local and long-distance calls being distorted, which necessitates a different network investment profile. On a personal level, users find they cannot make calls, and they miss calls when they are on-line longer than they think. The solution? Well, it appears that most of us just have to get a second phone line

For those systems polling regularly with very short hold times designed to minimize connection costs, it is even worse. Telephone signaling, control, and billing systems were never designed for such high rates of setup and clear down. So access can also be blocked by CPU overload.

But this is only the start. Network computing and TV access to the net through set-top boxes will introduce new on-line activities that could swell the population of users very fast. They will be totally reliant upon the telephone network for all applications and services. The problem will be the lack of sharing, and it looks like we need a new Mr. Erlang —and a new network model.

19

BEING ANALOGUE

In an increasingly digital world, being a predominantly analogue entity is getting tougher. Faster digital machines present a significant mismatch to us and our biosystems. At best, we can estimate we take in about 1 Gbit/s visually, but require about 7 Gbit/s for full head and eye tracking, and a full spatial model requires some 900 Gbit/s. Nonintrusive scanning mechanisms show this form of information as a reasonably localized flush of energy consumption or neural activity in our brain. The same is true of acoustic, tactile, taste, and smell stimulation, but to a much smaller degree, of course.

At a conservative estimate, and assuming we could use every corner of our brain, which we cannot, each of us could store about 5000 years worth of continuous conversation and about 5 years worth of continuous video. Well, on one plane, thank our lucky stars we are analogue and do forget. Our analogue memory system seems to have evolved to let information fade exponentially, and perhaps this is the stuff of dreams. The problem is that we have new IT-driven demands to remember and process increasingly more as we communicate, work, travel, and meet more people.

I have long considered computers to be my third lobe. They are the place where I store and process everything with greater precision than nature would normally allow my carbon-based wetware. So looking to the future, can these two worlds of analogue and digital forms coexist symbiotically? Can we really communicate directly with machines? Well, perhaps not for a while, it would seem, but all the indications are promising.

There have now been thousands of successful cochlea implants involving chips mounted inside the human head. They restore the hearing of those suffering severe hearing difficulties. From an engineering perspective you might suppose that connecting the correct carbon-based nerves into the correct silicon feeds would be a major problem, but it seems not to be so. The wife of a friend has been profoundly deaf for over 50 years and recently had cochlea implants. Being a smart lady, she set about tutoring her brain by using a talking book in conjunction with the printed page. Playing the talking book into her electronic ears and simultaneously reading the same words, she was having her first stilted conversations within weeks. After only a couple of years she has become remarkably proficient, and she is not alone; thousands are now emulating this process. Of course, what they hear might not be as good as the real thing, but it works. It is a beginning and our technology is, as yet, very crude.

Similar experiences are also recorded with prosthetics coupled directly into the human nervous system. There are also serious attempts at nervous system repair with silicon bypass, and there has been just one experiment with an artificial retina. The precise wiring diagram does not seem to matter, we no longer seem to have to obey the engineer's cable color code. While our electronics is immutable in its configuration, the human system seems able to reprogram the I/O to accommodate this limitation. What a miracle. Our very adaptable and analogue nature seems to be able to accommodate our engineering system limitations.

It is interesting that recent developments in optical storage and processing technology are seeing a swing back to analogue forms that are more efficient than digital electronics. We should reflect that our biological systems are actually an interesting mix of analogue and digital. Might this be where our true synergy lies, where carbon meets silicon, where the dominantly digital meets the dominantly analogue, where mind meets machine?

20

"He that has eyes to see and ears to hear may convince himself that no mortal can keep a secret. If his lips are silent, he chatters with his fingertips; betrayal oozes out of him at every pore."

Sigmund Freud (1905)

INSECURITY

The very idea of making a purchase by giving someone your charge card or bank account details over the telephone, or worse, the Internet, fills many people with fear. They see it as risky and very insecure. But these same people buy gasoline, food, and goods from stores and are very happy to hand over their cards so a copy can be made, complete with a legible signature. In doing so, they never question or worry about the honesty of the recipient of this prized and protected information.

I was recently challenged by a man who claimed that his digital mobile phone was 100 percent secure. This I refuted. When asked to divulge the secret of how I would listen to his conversation, I countered with the simplest of eavesdropping techniques: I would just sit at the side of him. People on mobile phones are seldom guarded in what they say as they assume themselves to be in some kind of acoustic bubble. So electronic crime does not always need fancy technology, just opportunism.

There is no such thing as security. It is a dream. Security is not an absolute quantity, only a relative commodity. The reality is that most security failures are attributable to human fallibility, bribery, and corruption. Granted, electronic break-ins are on the increase, but so is the theft of complete machines. And how is this so different from the world of paper? Well, only in its scale and apparent invisibility.

In contrast to modern technology, entire legal systems stand or fall by pen and ink, the human signature is legally binding and held as proof. It is also one of the easiest things to forge. Paper money, gold, and silver are easy to steal, but require physical action that is visible. Electronic crime on the other hand can introduce new dimensions of reach, scale, and anonymity.

So what of cryptography? Surely that is really secure. Well, not necessarily. For example, a modest home computer can search all the combinations in a 40-bit sequence in a week or so. With a mainframe this falls to a few seconds. More impressively, cracking codes lends itself to parallelism. So all we have to do is link tens of power PCs to realize a tremendous capability. No matter how long the sequence or code used, the computer to crack it will arrive sooner or later.

Of course, we can reduce the odds against electronic crime by changing code sequences on each operation, but this can be expensive and inconvenient. So I would put my money on the concatenation of several codes or simple overt and covert protection devices. If we spend $1000s, it is possible to recognize a face, voice, hand, fingerprint, and other biometrics with a billions-to-one chance of an error. However, for just a few $100s we can realize error probabilities around one in a thousand. Applying four or five of these techniques in succession can rapidly achieve error probabilities in the hundreds of billions to one. Super security can therefore be both low-cost and convenient.

Now, back to the original problem: When we wish to spend money, the vendor wants to know it is us and that we have the money to spend. We, on the other hand, should be gauging the honesty of the vendor and the security of the transaction. Ultimately, the weak link is the people involved, and it may be some time before machines can outsmart or catch us.

21

"What is the use of
a book without pictures
or conversation?"
Lewis Carroll, Alice in Wonderland

JUST PICTURE IT

An old Chinese proverb attributed to Confucius (~500 BC) states: I hear and I forget; I see and I remember; I do and I understand. Several thousand years ago, this was profoundly insightful. In a similar vein, Petronius Arbiter (~60 AD) observed that the most important message was the least expected one. The implications of such thinking ought to be even more obvious today. But when you look at our democracy, bureaucracy, and institutions, you could be convinced we had learnt nothing. Even the Internet is dominated by an infinity of words. What is this burdensome focus on text?

The world's libraries now store well over 100M original volumes. So in one sense, it is now easier to write the book you want rather than try to find it. But resting on these shelves are the Lord's Prayer (~70 words), the 23rd Psalm (115 words), and the Ten Commandments (135 words). These are the basic tenets by which a large percentage of the human race live. In contrast, the documentation, defining, and pricing of cabbages in the EEC consumes nearly 7000 words. This is almost five times as many as those used in the Declaration of Independence for the United States (1488 words). Why do we use unnecessary prose to describe everyday situations and objects? Have we lost the ability to be concise? Apart from wearing out our eyes, the sheer human effort needed to generate the mountains of words, the confusion they cause, and the storage space they demand beggars belief. Why not keep it simple? Why not use fewer words and more pictures?

43

Perhaps our processes of communication are becoming like the fast food industry: confused by the richness of options and the efficacy of quality and quantity. In the extreme, we have press, radio, and TV highly dependent on the snapshot, sound, and/or video bite. Seldom are we given the opportunity to judge on the basis of the full story. So very often it seems that really important issues hit the page and screen for the briefest of periods, while reams of paper and air time are devoted to the trivial and insignificant. Until recently, we have not had the network mechanisms to allow us our own individual in-depth analysis, but IT might ultimately provide the solution.

I have often pondered the strange phenomenon of the on-line newspaper, with the printed page reproduced directly on the screen verbatim. As far as I can see, no account has been taken of the change in medium—from printed page to network and PC. To ignore the ability to combine text and pictures with audio and video, let alone interaction, seems about as sensible as double entry bookeeping on a PC. By and large, a direct transfer from paper to screen is always a bad move.

When I was at school and college, I attended classes on communication and creative writing. Perhaps we now need courses on creative communication, which involves the simultaneous exploitation of all the variables offered by our developing technology. I cannot imagine that Shakespeare, Browning, and Dickens would have restricted themselves to quill, parchment, and paper if the multimedia choices we enjoy today had been available to them. My guess is they would have recorded their plays, verse, and stories using technology to the full. The world would not have been left to interpret exactly what they meant; all would have been much clearer and richer. Come to think of it, so might the law, the legislation of governments, and operational documents of companies and institutions.

22

"This 'telephone' has too many shortcomings to be seriously considered as a means of communication. The device is inherently of no value to us."

Western Union internal memo (1876)

PLEASE ANSWER ME

When we traveled less and telephones were all on the end of a wire, you could be reasonably sure of making direct contact with people. Today, our world has become more complex. In less than eight years more than 10 percent of all telephones have become mobile, with ever more fax and answering machines. How many times do you call someone to find they are out, indisposed, or have apparently been replaced by a machine? Telephone tag is becoming an international sport.

In the old days of lesser mobility there was a 98 percent chance someone would be at their place of work, and a 90 percent chance that they would be at the side of their fixed telephone. Call and rental charges were much higher then and calls shorter and fewer. So there was only about a 10 percent chance that you would get a busy signal, no reply, or nonavailability. For over 80 percent of the working day you could contact the person of your choice, and in most cases someone would answer the phone, talk to you, and take a message. How different today.

Many people now travel so much that they occupy their offices for only about 70 percent of the time, and business intensity sees them in conversation, meetings, and otherwise indisposed for 70 percent of the day. So we have a slice of the working population available to answer the telephone for only about 50 percent of the time. But there are more calls of longer duration, and a contact window of less than 35 percent is not uncommon. So if we do not get a busy signal, then for

45

at least 65 percent of the time a machine answers, or we are diverted to a series of unanswered extensions, to ultimately be ignored or answered by an unknowing human who takes a message.

Resorting to a mobile phone generally produces a marginal improvement with users switched on for more than 80 percent of the time. But there is still a 30 percent chance of the person being indisposed to the point of nonreply. So for about 50 percent of the time, call diversion or answering machines deal with the rest. In general, the contact window hovers just above 50 percent.

In part, this has all contributed to the growing popularity of voice mail, messaging, and e-mail for fixed and mobile working. They all put delay back into the communication process where it is required. This helps to relieve those suffering acute information overload, exacerbated by continual electronic interruptions. These relatively new modes of communication do not possess the distracting immediacy of the fixed and mobile telephone. Many people seem to have reached a point of needing to find a means of managing communication and information flow to restore a reasonable balance to the whole process. The limits to human communication, information I/O, and processing are now the fundamental limits to our activities. We are the weak link in the chain of progress.

A further debilitating problem beyond our limited ability to access, process, and I/O data is our inability to network. Even the Romans were aware of the problem and organized legions by tens or thereabouts. Modern companies and organizations often rediscover this fundamental limit to the span of human communication and control. In contrast, machines do not suffer from such limitations and can extend our abilities to thousands of people. But for us this means broadcast rather than dialogue. Within the next decade we are going to have to reassess the way we choose to talk to each other and machines. But the first priority is to get something intelligent to answer when we call.

23

"Mathematics is the door and key to the sciences."

Roger Bacon (1267)

MATHEMATICS and BIGGER BRAINS

As a student I was besotted by the power of mathematics and physical modeling. My enthusiasm was fueled by the fact that barring a few generalizing assumptions and simplifications of real-world situations, most of the problems I was presented with could be solved by one technique or another. For me, the power of the mathematical process, the training, clear thinking, and ability it invokes cannot be understated, and it is in stark contrast to the less quantifiable sciences and humanities.

Like everyone else, I was in an education system that lulled me into a false sense of security, as I was fed a continual diet of problems that had solutions. This convinced me that our universe was largely well behaved, with a few nonlinear areas that were difficult, but which could mostly be avoided. When I moved into industry, it came as a shock to find the converse was true. We can solve almost nothing, relatively speaking. Our universe is principally nonlinear, and we mostly get by with approximations to reality, or even gross misrepresentations. I am still surprised that we have been able to engineer and achieve as much as we have given the oft crudeness of our models and understanding of reality.

Reflecting upon this recently, I pondered the way we teach mathematics. Given the critical dependence of our civilization on the subject, it seems paradoxical that it lacks any general acclaim or popularity. For most people it usually invokes a dull ache, fear, and mysticism. Perhaps this is because the process of acquiring mathematical skills is generally protracted and painful. While it is often perceived as a nightmare topic, the truth is that with good teaching, most people can become reasonably competent. However, the time and effort needed to acquire even a modest capability can be excessive by today's standards.

When ancient people first attached a sharp stone to a stick to create a spear, they did not seek out a target and then apply a mathematical formula for the force and trajectory. They got by with trial and error, eventually leading to some exceptional encephalization of their brains over millennia. Not until Newton arrived did the physical and mathematical detail get attended too in a rigorous manner. To this day, we still teach our students from formula towards action and projectile. Worse, we divorce them from the physical reality through computers producing numbers to such accuracy that they obscure the uncertainties of the physical process.

Performing real experiments and making observations prior to mathematical modeling and measuring the outcome of trials against predictions is powerful stuff. But combining this with on-screen modeling introduces a further level of clarity and dimension for understanding. Plotting a trajectory is only the first stage. Introducing the influence of air turbulence and throwing action variations adds much more depth of understanding and insight to the complexity involved.

Highly complex systems, such as airflow over an aircraft wing, gas flow in a turbine, fluid motion, and neural networks, defy mathematical analysis for all but the most stable situations. Nonlinearity and chaos dominate the real world and may always fall outside our established routes to solution and understanding. But it is in this realm that we are likely to make the most exciting discoveries and advances. What we require is that intuitive feel for what the final outcome is likely to be and the sensitivities of the processes to input changes. Perhaps the computer can be our stone on a stick, the means by which we move on to understand. Only this time, it will be computers that enjoy the encephalization, and not us.

24

"We have a layer of clay that prevents anything moving either way—up or down. The layer is middle management."

Heini Lippuner, Ciba CEO (1991)

DELAYERING

Traditionally, most organizations have been strictly hierarchical and based upon the power and control of individuals or individual groups. Steep pyramids of power and laws have been the name of the game for centuries. However, technological change is now challenging this established and well-tried model. It is effectively shaking out the need for the many layers of management dictated by old technologies and wisdoms.

When the U.S. Army invaded Granada, a single GI came under fire from ten policemen. Being outnumbered, he called HQ by radio and asked what he was to do. The reply was a singular order: Shoot them. It later transpired that this order was given by a four-star general, in person. So the question arose: What are all the intervening ranks for, and what were they doing?

Desert Storm saw troops without an approved personal Navistar system. So back home, Mom and Pop went to Radio Shack and bought $300 GPS units and mailed them direct to their sons in the featureless desert. It also turned out that the most reliable piece of IT was a laserjet printer purchased from an electronics store. So the question arose: Why bother with military specification and procurement?

These examples reflect technologies that induce fundamental operational and organizational change. No wonder companies are downsizing and delayering. Improved communication and computing allow the old style management chains and processes to be bypassed. Companies that had five layers of management can now get by with only two, and as a result they become more dynamic and responsive.

It is as if the intermediate layers were in place to stop organizations from becoming successful. If true, it is not by design, but more by culture and tradition. Managers who act as information and control intermediaries create unnecessary delays and inaction. Holding onto information, people, and control used to be a way of maintaining position and staying employed. Today, it is the kiss of death for the individual and the company.

So why do modern armies still have all those ranks when commanders have direct radio access to all their troops? Well, it appears to be a combination of mindset, tradition, and the fear and risk of change. No one apart from a despot wants to gamble with human lives. But this is not a problem if all the armies in the world maintain the status quo. It is only a problem if one army makes a successful change and becomes a far more effective and superior machine. In modern business there is no status quo. Many have moved or are on the move, and competition leaves us with no choice. We have to become more efficient and responsive. Management delayering and outsourcing on an increased scale are inevitable if we are to keep markets and maintain low costs.

The really successful and fast developing companies are now more like amorphous blobs than hierarchical armies of ranked officers. Although production lines and processes still demand the stability of structure, increased levels of automation put even this under threat. So we can expect more pressure from the ever-shortening lifetimes of products and industries, with most of us facing more change than all previous generations.

It should be recognized that none of this can be realized by blindly cutting out people. Without a considered and coordinated investment in technology, new working practices, processes, and most important of all, education and training, it can all go badly wrong. To tackle one or two, and not all facets of change, can be fatal. But getting it right can mean survival and a very healthy bottom line.

25

STRAIGHT IN THE EYE

Ever since the invention of television, we seem to have had a fixation for a windows mode of viewing. Although reasonably adequate for entertainment, it is severely limiting for IT, and especially portable devices. The arrival of the liquid crystal display has made the limitations even more obvious. With a contrast ratio and brightness a fraction of the cathode ray tube—severe washout in bright sunlight, poor or zero operation at low temperatures, slow response times, and numerous optical artifacts, they are far from ideal. Perhaps it's time for a change, time for a new technology.

Why do we take a beam of electrons and illuminate a panel that we then view at a distance? Why not take a beam of photons and inject it directly into the eye to create a pure image on our retina? All the intermediate stages of conversion from electron bombardment to phosphor excitation and photon generation only detract from the efficiency and final quality. Why do it that way when it is possible to take over the entire visual cortex and create a sense of being somewhere else—real or artificial?

It is now reasonable to suppose that a laser-based projection system could be mounted on a contact lens or spectacle frame. It turns out, however, that this dream of an active contact lens is beyond today's technology. The power supply currently presents problems, and the circuit lithography (printing) required is just not fine enough—yet. But a head-mounted device is feasible. We therefore have in prospect new windows into information worlds without the burden of large boxes of technology.

Along with computers that talk to us, we might now perceive a world where they share our visual field in much the same way that "The Terminator" was able to simultaneously view real-world images and digital readouts. As a species we have an amazing ability to multi-task; reading a newspaper while listening to the radio is perhaps one of the most common occurrences. In contrast, television demands our attention and is an ideal instrument of distraction. Curiously, it would appear that we have an innate ability to live in more than one world at once through multiple visual and acoustical inputs. Information from the real world can enter one eye and one ear, and at the same time, information from computer-generated worlds can take over the remaining organs.

Now we come to the thorny problem of protocol, convention, and what is acceptable. We are extremely perceptive and very conscious of facial expression and eye contact. When I look at you and I can see an animated graph, my favorite TV program, or a page of text hovering in free space above your head, will we still be able to communicate? This might be tricky if the data is your CV, medical record, or a briefing on your company and your activities.

The smallest mobile telephone now weighs only 3.5 ounces, and our world hovers on a move away from the PC in the direction of network computing. And there is a growing enthusiasm and interest in body-worn computers and communicators. Put all these together with a head-mounted projector constructed from lasers the size of a salt crystal and we have a very different world in prospect. But it doesn't stop there, for along with microminiature projectors come microminiature cameras and the possibility of shared worlds. At that point, what I see, you see; what I read, you read; and vice versa.

26

"Our memories are card indexes consulted and then returned in disorder by authorities whom we do not control."

Cyril Connolly (1944)

A UNIHEAP ON THE BEACH

Somewhere in your deepest memory is probably a scene at the seaside with parents and family when you were 10 or so years old. If you think about that day, it will be recalled in reasonably vivid detail that you might consider to be fact. But should you have a photograph from the day, the difference between reality and recollection will be very significant. Why is this? Well, we are more analogue than digital, and our memory process is Hebbian, that is, reinforcement followed by exponential decay with time. So unless we regularly refresh our memories, events and remembrances start to part company.

In stark contrast, machines are dominantly digital and therefore record everything with precision and longevity. Couple this with the human tendency to record everything and throw nothing away and we are faced with mountains of worthless data. We are often data rich and information poor. In the paper world of the past, many of us instituted regimes of yearly culls of filing cabinets. Files would be taken out and reduced to a tenth of their thickness by mercilessly dispatching huge amounts of paper to the shredding machine. That regime has now been reborn in the cyclic culling of information on PCs and mainframes. But it has gotten much worse. Multiple copies and versions on multiple machines in multiple locations. How do we cope? Well, I don't think we can. Trying to operate two PCs in two locations and keep them in sync seems impossible. Add a laptop and the level of difficulty seems to accelerate away from us. So what to do?

Although machines are digital, it is not beyond us to introduce Hebbian mechanics to exponentially cull information triggered by its lack of usage. In many organizations information now has a half-life of six months or less. And yet we still record and store it as if it was of value, which it is not. As a first step in this direction, software can check on the last access date of information and after a predetermined time remove all color, logos, and nonessential information. Later, automatic summarizing can cut documents down to their very essence. Progressively doing this places documents in a fit state to be destroyed, or merely left as headstones in some remote and little used memory space.

Such systems are not difficult to engineer and do work, but I have to confess to also destroying vast amounts of information and never filing it in the first place. People often confuse communication quality and quantity, and certainly when dealing with some institutions, it is often better to toss rather than even attempt to read and file.

In another corner of my life I have experimented with a novel way of filing. This I call "uniheap." Because I come from a world of paper, I have been conditioned to putting electronic information in folders and neatly storing it on my hard disc. Indeed, this is a very useful and powerful mechanism for creating order, stability, and efficiency. However, in the world of e-mail that comes thick and fast, there is no time to file, no time to sort, and merely throwing all the messages into a big pile seems sufficient. The search and find capability of a PC brings to the fore all messages on any topic or from any group or person almost instantly, and then they can just be thrown back on the heap. I suspect my mind works like this too. If only I could get it to cull all the irrelevant and never used items, I might have enough capacity for the rest of my life.

27

"The chief reason warfare is still with us is . . . . the simple fact that no substitute for this final arbiter in international affairs has yet appeared on the political scene."

Hannah Arendt (1972)

VIRTUAL WARS

By and large, young people have an affinity for IT through early exposure and fearless experimentation. They prefer not to read handbooks or ask questions, but to just do it. Most parents and older people do not share this mindset. They come from a different world and lack exposure and experience.

Even as a technologist, multifunction buttons and other interface twists sometimes give me grief. It took me a while to discover that ejecting an audiocassette from my car radio meant depressing the play button for four seconds. It wasn't obvious to me, but it was for my young son. In this case the ability divide was not one of technophile and technophobe, it was just a mindset difference. As a general rule such fractures between generations are age-related through experience and expectation, a bit like acquiring a bad golf swing.

For the very young, the process of learning to interface with technology is done by raw experimentation, trial and error. You get on a machine and you fly until you crash, and then you reset and start again. This is repeated until you become proficient. As a process it is incremental and handbook free, like learning to walk and run. While older generations might view playing computer games as a waste of time, they are a sure way of overcoming technophobia and acquiring essential skills.

There is no doubt that IT has a great potential to create couch potatoes and unthinking people, but on the other hand, it also is a great enabler and means of educating faster than ever before. Children are like sponges for information, experience, and understanding. With IT they can go at their own pace and feel unabashed at experimenting. They are never intimidated by mere technology, only people. In some studies it has been found that youngsters can absorb information 50 percent faster and retain 80 percent more in the pictographic and interactive world of multimedia. In some cases it is even greater; in others, far less. The advantage is strongly linked to the topic—unfortunately, we do not seem to have discovered a means of burning the multiplication tables or spelling and grammar into the human brain other than by rote.

Talking to a young virtual pilot recently, I discovered an encyclopedic mind able to recount the performance and specification of many aircraft from World War II to the present day. His knowledge came from the direct experience of flying them on both sides in the many theatres of war since 1939. How powerful a method of learning and understanding—and not without some extraordinary breadth. At the same time, it turned out that his spatial awareness was also unusual. He saw the screen as window on the inside of a sphere, just a portal to a world of virtual war. Interestingly, with the aid of radar, his memory, and spatial awareness, he was able to visualize the location of tens of aircraft in a simulated dog fight. Most impressive of all was his developed sense of combat strategy. He played to win against impossible odds.

This youngster was also able to visualize complex interactions in three dimensions. When confronted with the Pythagorean triangle, the sum of the squares appeared obvious. This was followed by the conceptual leap to 3D, and then to n dimensional space—obvious. Well, 25 years ago it was not obvious to me nor, I suspect, many others. Powerful stuff these games, so powerful he was prompted to ask the question: Why do we have real wars and kill real people when it can be done on the screen and no one gets hurt?

28

> *"Knowledge is the most democratic source of power."*
>
> Alvin Toffler (1990)

WHO KNOWS?

I know what I know, and you know what you know. How come our computers know nothing? Ask any human a question on any subject and they will be almost instantly conscious of their range and level of understanding. A few moments thought will see them espousing all they know. Give them minutes or hours, and the depth of delivery may grow significantly as they plumb the recesses of their memories and/or revisit a book or library. Searching out more detail by any mechanism takes no prompting, only opportunity. In stark contrast, machines just sit there oblivious to the knowledge they store, the networks they can access, and others of their species that may be able to help. They lack a consciousness and understand nothing. They are mere blocks of silicon, gold, and copper, computing engines devoid of true intelligence. Without the prompting of a human hand to make connections, to search networks and other machines for specific data, they just sit there as if comatose. It is as if they are sleeping, waiting to be awakened.

So what is this consciousness we possess? Theologians, philosophers, and scientists have pondered this question for eons, often relating it to some soul or higher level of inner being. From an engineering perspective, it appears to be a combination of sensory experience, memory, and an overlay of search, find, and correlate software. It's an ability to take a word, phrase, or concept and retrieve all related memories, pull together the core features, and then deliver them appropriately finessed for the occasion—quite a trick. Of course, the key question is: how? And a key objective is to recreate this kind of facility, and more, in machines so they can aid and assist us further.

The hard wiring or firing of the human brain (wetware) gives us few or no clues as to our conscious being, the way we function or operate. In our mental abilities, we appear more or less supreme in the animal kingdom. But we also see competition on the horizon; increasingly intelligent machines are coming. So there are two basic choices, to try and engineer a conscious thought process into machines or just wait for it to evolve naturally. To do the latter will find us still ignorant of the process, while attempting the former would give us at least a transitory understanding of the starting point. It might also give a few clues and pointers regarding our own sophistication and functionality. But it can be reasonably assumed that once conscious, machines will evolve more rapidly than carbon life and may just leave us behind.

The determinism of mathematics has already been used to predict that machines will never be truly intelligent and conscious. But this is more likely to be a limitation of the mathematics, mathematicians, and their models rather than anything fundamental. With our central processor (brain) of over 10,000,000,000 neurons, the analysis of other life forms, such as worms and ants, with far less than 1000, has so far defied our innate intelligence. Further more, we should recollect how our limited and largely linear mathematical abilities recently precluded flight, breaking the sound barrier, and space travel.

True machine intelligence is most likely to emerge from noisy and highly nonlinear entities, rather than today's deterministic systems that enjoy massive connectivity linking relatively simple and almost wholly predictable processors (neurons). The very essence of biological minds is their variability, uncertainty, fuzzy processing and memory decay with time. In short, we are much more random than we first appear. Machines, on the other hand, will have the advantage of combining all these attributes—at will. Once they know, they will know forever.

29

"Computers in the future may weigh no more than 1.5 tons."

Popular Mechanics (1949)

THE OFFICE YOU WEAR

Only five years ago, I carried a large and very heavy briefcase full of paper. Today my case is a fraction of the size, virtually paperless, but twice as heavy. The reason? It is now full of batteries for my laptop and mobile phone, plus cables, connectors, chargers, screwdrivers, alligator clips, and all the sundries necessary for a mobile electronic office. This miracle of technology is now a necessity for my new mode of management: If you're not on-line, you don't exist. Although this mobile office is extremely compact and powerful, it is gradually extending the length of my arms as I lug it from one location to another.

A critical look at the electronic functionality I now carry reveals that a considerable degree of integration is possible. For example, combined wristwatch/pagers, or even a complete cellular telephone, are available at a price. The laptop too can be condensed down to an organizer or PDA with considerable savings in size and weight. What chance then for a complete integration of all my electronics into one mobile entity?

In the same way the carriage clock evolved to become body furniture, the wristwatch, then perhaps we might expect to see an office we can wear. The principal limitation to this dream is the requirement for batteries. Today, economically priced cellular telephones employ three integrated circuits. However, it is feasible to reduce this down to one, requiring only one watt of power. Similarly, a laptop computer can be reduced to two chips consuming just two watts, with another three watts for the LCD screen.

A further impediment to realizing the office I wear is the requirement for a keyboard. But perhaps this could be overcome by voice I/O. Today, voice synthesis is just about adequate for text to speech. Speech to text still leaves a lot to be desired and will probably require a further five years of evolution before it can fully replace the keyboard.

An intermediate solution might be tenable with the minimal keypad or PDA stylus input. Alternatively, a foldaway keyboard for pocket and case transport could be plugged in when necessary, along with a head-mounted screen giving high-definition access directly into the eye. All of the piece parts are available now and such a device is feasible. However, it leaves us with one critical problem to solve, that of power storage and the requirement for large batteries.

Sitting still, we radiate approximately 60 watts from our torsos and heads. When animated, this can exceed 100 watts and is a potential source of power to drive an office you wear. Alternatively, the process of walking and moving at a casual rate can generate more than 10 watts. It would appear, therefore, that all solutions to realize a wearable office are at hand. We are our own power station.

As a general rule, the human race makes progress by incremental change, with slight extensions of existing paradigms that do not upset or compromise existing working practices, protocols, and social sensibilities. If I were talking to you face-to-face and someone interrupted the conversation, we would think him or her rude. However, if during our conversation someone were to call by telephone, I would feel totally relaxed about momentarily ignoring you to answer the telephone. This has become an acceptable mode of operation. How then will you respond when, mid-conversation, I gaze into a head-mounted screen, adjust controls on my wrist, and commence a new conversation with some ethereal being or machine?

30

*"Emotional bits are
the most important bits"*

Bran Ferran,
Walt Disney Research (1996)

EMOTIONAL ICONS

Just as the PC has made the transition to the iconic world, it is plain to see that such a world has a limited future. For over 15 years icons have become well established as a rapid means of navigating computer environments. But they are flat, static, and only able to convey limited information. Moreover, icons now clutter the desktop to the point that they obscure the view. This is compounded by the layering of pages and applications. It is often impossible to simultaneously see your work and your icons. Is this then the end of the line for icons?

Perhaps icons could have meaningful shapes and be dynamic and interactive, changing color and shape with use and status. With a modest amount of artificial intelligence, they could mimic many of our human traits, for example, to seek our attention and help us or hide away until a more appropriate time. Giving them personality, contextual reactions, and perhaps facial expressions would increase their ability to communicate with us. The addition of a voice, the spoken word, or at least indicative noises would not go amiss either.

The next obvious feature would be to put them into a 3D rather than 2D world so we could realize the additional freedom of position and movement. We could then be guided in decision making and information navigation in new and novel ways. All of this is possible on the PC platform today. So perhaps the iconic world has not had its day. Perhaps it is only just beginning.

How many times have you mouse clicked a bad decision, or a finger slipped and you lost valuable information? How many times have you been unable to find that part of a pull-down menu you require? How many times have you filled your screen, or a window, with multiple developments of the same entity? How many times have you had difficulty navigating a mass of files and applications ? Probably too many.

Reactive, emotional, and intelligent icons can help avoid such problems. Personality features responding to our actions, material content, sensitivity, security, decisions, and state of development give humanized clues to steer us. Human communication is full of subtlety and nonobvious responses that add significant depth to our words and gestures. The raising of an eyebrow, curl of the lip, tilting of the head, slight change in posture, all convey thousands of bits of information. In contrast, computers are dead and unresponsive.

What other features might we give our emotional icons? Probably as many human ones as possible. A friendly icon could respond by moving toward us as we reach out into the information space. A nervous icon might shiver at a potentially risky action, while a defensive icon might erect a barrier and increase it's height as we approach. An unsure icon might retreat and become elusive. Only when we force this icon into a corner, when it cannot escape, can it be activated. A message icon might have the sender's face and be animated to flag urgency.

Realizing the full potential of such an iconic world, we might ultimately envisage reaching out to touch and feel substance. This would add another powerful dimension that would parallel humans shaking hands. Icons could then pull or push us, guide and be guided within a virtual data world.

Among the AI community, it has been suggested that we should not anthropomorphize computers because they might not like it. I'm not so sure. What I do know is that I have been silicomorphized for over 20 years and I don't like it either. And now I want a humanized machine.

31

"Science and technology multiply around us. To an increasing extent they dictate the languages in which we speak and think. Either we use those languages, or we remain mute."

J. G. Ballard (1974)

BOOKS AND CHICKENS

Ask most people which is the dominant language on planet earth, and they will reply with either—English or Chinese. A good guess, but they would be wrong. Binary is now dominant with computers and machines having more conversations every working day than the sum total of mankind going back to the birth of Eve. This situation should not be vexing, it does not lessen our ability to survive and prosper, quite the reverse. And, yet from the vitriolic denial and ignorance of technology lauded by many in the media and society you might think that the reverse was the case.

There appears to be an implicit assumption that as technology advances, we have to regress. Yet with the invention of the plow we are able to create more food, with the axe with were able to cut more wood and build, and with a bow and arrow we became very effective hunters. Today, very few of us have to use any of these instruments of production and killing—we have moved on. In the same way as the printing press negated the need for thousands of quill pen guiding monks, IT is empowering people, realizing new skills and allowing them to do new things. In fact, they can now experience and achieve far more than any previous generation. A typical Ph.D. student or engineer now has an output hundreds of times greater than their counterparts of 20 years ago, and each generation sees more.

For those who fear for the future of books, I would pose this question; where is most information now stored and presented? If your reaction is the printed page and the library then you are mistaken. Electronic libraries and display systems now present orders of magnitude, more information than was ever recorded on paper. Ink on paper has already gone the same way as the quill pen, yet we can still read and write, and we still like a good book, and quite rightly. It is important to remember that technology is our slave and not the other way round. We should not deny technology and neither should we use it where it is inappropriate. Paper is very user friendly, but limited.

Technology has always been an alternative means of meeting new objectives and doing new things, and as such is an opportunity to create new worlds. In business, medicine, production and education IT has a major role to play. It is no longer feasible to organize the logistics of a nation, or the planet on the basis of the written word by hand on a piece of paper. Reverting to that process would see chaos and millions of casualties—people would simply starve for want of communication. Nor, is it possible to go back to the days of Aristotle and word of mouth teaching. Thinking how a chicken works can be a lot of fun and very satisfying, but in reality taking a chicken apart, or better, building a chicken is far more productive. It is also one of the few routes to true understanding.

For most of us it is not feasible to do experiments with a real or metaphoric chicken. But it is possible to participate in dissections and constructions of almost anything on screen. This is conducive to greater creativity and output, but it will not be a successful prospect if the architects of IT do not take into account our human limitations and preferences.

32

*"It's kind of fun
to do the impossible."*
Walt Disney (1945)

FROM KIRK TO PICARD

If ever I had a dream of mobile communication, it was fueled by my Tuesday night experiences as a student in the 1960s. Tuesday nights were special. The TV room would be packed with anticipation, people waiting to see James T. Kirk beam down to some unknown planet. His first act was always to confirm safe arrival through his fliptop communicator. This remarkable and obviously analogue device worked convincingly, with the occasional twist of a rotary knob to fine-tune, avoid static, and gain clear communication. At that time mobile radios used by the police, emergency services, and taxis still employed thermionic valves (no transistors) and were the size of a briefcase. So what Captain Kirk had was barely credible.

Thirty years later, Jean Luc Picard just wears a badge, and a stroke of his hand is all it takes to contact anyone. Communication is obviously digital: always clear and concise; no numbers to remember, buttons to push, or knobs to adjust; all very natural and easy to use. But this dream is now much closer. Today we have mobile phones the size of chocolate bars that cost almost nothing. Only a decade ago, the first cellular phones were the size and weight of a small briefcase, and the so-called pocket phones the size of a brick. So perhaps we are catching up with the future.

The primary physical limitations to mobile phone size are the batteries, keyboard, and display—in that order. Hard-to-read and decode multifunction displays and buttons and an assumed microphone-to-ear distance half that of a human head often demand unnatural acts when trying to make contact and talking. However, this all seems necessary in the race to reduce size and cost.

Laptops already have built-in modems and power supplies, and soon the entire digital phone will also be integrated into the one device. So size, dictated by human fingers, visual acuity, and physical strength, will be the ultimate limiter. As a result, we currently stand in danger of creating a new species of human, with longer arms, very thin fingers, and shorter sight. However, the market has already seen the pocket organizer combined with a mobile phone, and more will follow. So what happens next?

Moore's law tells us chip density will double at <18 month intervals for at least another two decades and probably more. So complete mobile phones will be realized on a single chip. But there is a more fundamental change afoot. Voice command and control may do away with the need for both a keypad and display.

It is already possible to talk to a machine to gain directory advice and buy and sell goods. But when we are on the move, background acoustic noise from cars, trains, and people is a major limiter. The simple addition of a lightweight headset with noise canceling is an obvious and long-awaited addition for those who want to drive, ride, walk, and talk. But then there are other possibilities, such as adaptive noise cancellation; constant sound level relative to background noise can be engineered to adapt to variations in head position and location.

All the technology now looks ripe, and the Star Trek badge communicator is feasible. The only debate is where to locate the bulk of the intelligence. To carry it all with us is not possible today, so it will have to be embedded in the network. However, as chip technology advances, there will be a gradual migration of intelligence back to the badge to realize a truly distributed intelligence for the 21st century.

33

The earth is mankind's ultimate haven ... When it trembles ... it's as though one of God's cheques has bounced.

Gilbert Adair (1989)

NETQUAKES

For many threatening or disaster situations we have developed reference scales to calibrate the severity of individual events. From earthquakes, hurricanes, storms, pollen count, or pollution we have simple and singular metrics. But there are events both natural and self-inflicted that are threatening and stressful and remain uncalibrated in any way. Birth, death, illness, being mugged, getting divorced, and changing jobs are common examples. Recently, IT has added a raft of new mechanisms to the menu, like changing or upgrading computers and/or their software, operating bugs, and crashes. But in an increasingly virtual world of electronic commerce, perhaps the most critical calamity will be the network crash. When nets crash, virtual organizations stop working. Little or nothing can be done. So how might we calibrate their severity?

So far, there have been relatively few network failures on a scale great enough to cause catastrophic economic disruption. One exception was in 1991 when 40 million people lost their telephone service for 19 hours on the east coast of the U.S. Computer networks have only recently assumed great economic importance, and quantifying the impact of failures may become vital if future network design is to be correctly focused. The key difficulty is the diversity of the failure types, causes, mechanisms, avoidance, and customer impact. What you are doing when there is a crash is important. In the worst case valuable work and information can be lost or corrupted. So we might contemplate a simple means of ranking network failures so they can be readily understood by nonspecialists. Perhaps the Richter scale for earth-quakes could be modified to meet that need. After all, it brings the advantage of an established familiarity and intuitive feel across a broad range of potential users. For any simple linear measure, network outages vary over many orders of magnitude, so a logarithmic, Richter-like scale seems highly appropriate.

While absolute accuracy may be important to those investigating outages or seeking to protect networks from them in the future, it may not be a strong general requirement. An outage in the early hours of the morning has arguably far less impact on people than the identical event at peak working times. Also, the level of attention to an outage is likely to diminish with distance from the affected area, so a measure needs to be independent of these effects.

When Steven Hawking was writing *A Brief History of Time*, he was advised that book sales would halve for every mathematical equation included. So he opted for just one equation, and I decided to do the same here. A "netquake" measure based on down time and number of people affected seems a sensible first step. So, following the approach of Richter, we define the customer impact of a netquake as: $Q = \log_{10} NT$, where N is the number of computer terminals affected, and T is total down time.

On the earthquake scale, a magnitude 6.0 event has special signif-icance, because it marks the fuzzy boundary between minor and major events. So we might calibrate a magnitude 6.0 netquake to be repre-sented by 100 computer terminals off-line for 10,000 seconds (28 hours). But note: 10 terminals for 100,000 seconds (28 hours), or 1000 terminals for 1000 seconds (16.8 minutes), and so on, would give the same result.

Earthquakes in excess of magnitude 7.0 are considered major events and in a local geographical sense are rare. The same is true of electronic networks, but the notion of geography is different. Computer terminals can be distributed across the planet. So netquakes can be dis-tributed and concentrated in business or sector space, and not neces-sarily geographical space.

34

*"Integrity without knowledge
is weak and useless,
and knowledge without integrity
is dangerous and dreadful."*

Samuel Johnson (1759)

BEWARE OF THE DOGS

Only a short time ago the net was almost exclusively populated by academics and professionals exchanging information and ideas in an open, candid, and very productive manner. It was almost like a gentleman's club, with protocols, understanding, and an unstated code of ethics largely observed by all. More recently, the net population has exploded, and its nature as a medium has changed beyond recognition. This was reflected in a recent cartoon I saw where two dogs were portrayed sitting at a PC typing. One is looking at the other and saying, "The great thing about the net is, no one knows you are a dog."

This cartoon caused me both to chuckle and think about the nature of the medium and the dogs as metaphor for subtle change. When we meet people in the flesh, we immediately start to gauge their qualities. Clothing, mannerisms, choice of words, and body language give us initial impressions of sincerity and trustworthiness. We also assess the possibilities for cooperation, working relationships, and friendship, continually refining our perceptions in real time. Interestingly, it is becoming important to do this faster and more accurately as IT and travel speed up human interaction. We can now find ourselves meeting people a few times for short periods but still having to make commitments and important decisions.

When we use the telephone, a similar process of assessment occurs, based solely on conversation, tone, and responses to questions, propositions, and answers. Even in a written letter there are subtle clues that allow us to build a mental model of the correspondent. Letter headings, physical address, font, handwriting, signature, content, and style all help us relax and become friendly or stiff, cautious, and defensive.

How different is the world of e-mail. Communication is rapid, brusque, and efficient, but where are the clues? Is it a dog or a friend? Often we cannot tell until after the event. Friends will be open and honest, protect messages and treat them as private conversations, and broadly observe the normal protocols and behavior we see in much of society. The rest can be graded from the naive and careless to the pernicious and mischievous. They copy messages to individuals who should never have seen them or broadcast the contents to a public audience. The most difficult to deal with are those who quote out of context or cut and paste modified text under your name and header. Presumably they derive some perverse pleasure from this process, but they are definitely the dogs, and are dangerous.

A friend once observed that I write as I speak, and I guess it is true. For me, the process of trying to effect good communication pervades all my activities. As far as I can tell, my persona in the flesh is the same as on the telephone, video conferencing, radio and TV, letters, and e-mail. By nature, I always try to go straight for the kernel of a situation or problem, to conserve energy, and maximize my contribution. Curiously, for me anyway, I find this not to be the case for a good deal of the human race. I observe people saying, writing, and mailing things they would never say face-to-face. It is as if technology affords them some cloaking device, so they release parts of their personalities not normally visible. I do not decry this when used positively; I see some brilliant communicators who use this to great advantage. It can be a terrific skill. For many of us, however, I suspect we need a new notice on the road to the superhighway: Beware of the Dogs.

35

"Shoes are the first adult machines we are given to master."

Nicholson Baker (1988)

YOU'RE NOT WEARING MY SOCKS

If I walked into your office and asked to use your pen, telephone, copier, or fax machine, the chances are you would willingly agree and think nothing of it. You might even let me sit at your desk. But if I asked if I could use your personal computer, you would probably react as if I had asked to borrow your socks. Isn't it curious how we personalize technology and then become so blasé that we think nothing of it. As a child I remember cameras, radios, televisions, and telephones being prized items—and a big deal. They were definitely a measure of status and wealth. Asking to borrow or use someone else's took a deal of courage; you just did not do that sort of thing unless it was an emergency. All such items were relatively scarce, fragile, expensive, and mostly luxuries. Today, these technologies are incredibly reliable, low-cost, and in abundant supply. So they are no longer prized, no longer luxuries. They are now necessities, and just using them is the norm.

Why, then, are personal computers still in that ancient category of prized possessions? Well, they are certainly as expensive as the sparse technological luxuries of 40 years ago. But there is, I think, much more. We invest a lot of time organizing our machines and filling them with our most valuable possession—information. The thought of someone changing or rearranging our bits or chancing upon those bits that we don't want them to see is more than we can bear or risk. Probably the accidental corruption of our data and a sys-

71

tem or disc crash is what we fear most. For many of us, the removal of
the PC or the loss or damage of data on a hard drive would be something of a catastrophe that would cost us dearly. We would just stop
working for days while we rebuilt our virtual office and workshop. No
screen/no work is often the norm now .

It's not surprising then that most of us see a PC as a really personal
item, an extension of us, like our home, clothes, and jewelry. Someone
entering our world of data and IT is akin to the prospect of being burgled
or mugged. I wonder if we will react in the same way when we have networked computers with limited personal and local information storage
and processing capability. Perhaps not. At that point the computer will
have assumed a similar level of depersonalization as the telephone,
radio, and TV. Access to those bits we don't want other people to reach
will be easy to control and limit. And our applications (Applets) will be
a communal facility anyway, like a bus or a taxi, just hired for the period of use. Moreover, it will be a world where we can access our personal
information from afar using any convenient terminal PC, kiosk, or organizer in any company or location, public or private.

After network computing, we can expect combined computers and
communicators we wear with voice access and interaction, optional
head-mounted visual systems for animation and pictographic immersion, and artificial agents that do our bidding and generally look after
us. Ultimately, the technology may become invisible as it is embedded
into the fabric of buildings, vehicles, clothing, and other personal items
that think. We can also anticipate that it will become humanized and
able to develop personas to suit us and our specific needs. At this point
the socks syndrome will probably reappear as the technology becomes
more than a piece of technology and more a part of us, truly personal,
just like socks.

36

SYMBIOTIC MACHINES

Over the past few years I have progressively honed up all the computers in my life to the peak of processing fitness. Each machine sees me regularly running a diagnosis pack, repairing bad blocks, poor links, and corrupted addresses. Doing this every fortnight or so also sees me throwing away unwanted software and defragging the hard discs. All machines are always in tip-top condition, with enough RAM to allow the simultaneous operation of between 8 and 15 applications. They also have the intelligence to flag memory and operating stress by changing the desktop screen color from deep blue to light blue to light green to light pink as a crash point is approached. Once up and running, they are left operational with, at worst, just the monitors switched off. By any reckoning I consider this to be a pretty slick set of powerful and stable systems.

Of course, these machines do crash. All systems do; it is something we seem to have to live with. But on average, when everything is behaving itself, I have it down to a one in 3 to 4 week occurrence. So I guess I had every right to feel reasonably smug and capable when listening to the woes of others with three or four crashes a morning. However, a new pair of hands arrived in the shape of a collaborating staff member, who in a new experiment required direct access to my machines. With bravado, I explained how good my systems were, how solid and reliable, and how well I looked after them. And with a, "Just get to it; you cannot possibly upset my

73

computers." The hands made a start. To my astonishment, they were in multiple crash mode within 15 minutes. Applications and operations that would run faultlessly for me just presented a trail of grief for this newcomer. What was happening?

Desperately investigating this phenomenon at length, I found no logical explanation. It was as if I had some secret symbiosis with these computers and the stranger did not. Surely my machine was not smart enough to tell us apart and then inflict some secret trial by crash on this newcomer. Well, not quite. However, as far as I could tell, I had been quietly tutored not to touch the mouse when my browser was doing its stuff, to avoid doing much at all when sharing my hard disc with others, and so on. I had been subject to a subliminal process of conditioning by my machines, and perhaps I had not been so smart after all.

I watched the newhands over a few days, a week, a month, as they gradually gained the acceptance of my machines and the crash rate gradually fell to twice a day, once a day, once every couple of days. Here they reached a plateau of stability and unfortunately came to the end of the experiment. They never did achieve my enviable condition and left me slightly concerned. Just how do I do it? Is operating a computer really like playing a musical instrument? Is our technology becoming much more sentient and tuning us to its foibles?

Moving to my laptop, which is only a fraction of the size of my other machines, with a drastically pruned down operating system and application set, I decided on a rematch. The same newcomer moved into my crash league almost instantly. In fact, it turned out to be very difficult to crash this system, and when it happened, it was through a pattern I recognized. So perhaps we do enjoy a symbiosis with computers that gets ever critical and interesting with size and complexity.

37

"The village had institutionalized all human functions in forms of low intensity. . . . Participation was high and organization was low. This is the formula for stability."

Marshall McLuhan (1964)

CITY OR VILLAGE?

Established wisdom and business practice say that if you live in a village, you have to do everything, but if you live in a city, then you can afford to specialize. The gurus tell us that small is beautiful and the end of giant corporations is nigh. What is happening? Truth is, the vast majority of businesses are already small to medium. Even in the tiger economies of Asia they overshadow the giants in terms of the numbers employed.

One way of viewing current developments is to see corporations as the system integrators. These producers of cars, aircraft, and consumer goods no longer manufacture all of the piece parts. Some of them manufacture nothing; they just assemble the components as supplied. They no longer cut the grass or provide food or security guards either. Everything has been outsourced. Vertical integration has been overtaken by virtualization. No company, no matter how big, has all the resources necessary to bring product to market. Technological developments and demand are just moving too fast for the old model to work.

An unfortunate side effect for the small- to medium-sized business has been the increased potential to go bust through corporate and market fickleness. Many businesses have too many eggs in one basket, and some have only one basket. How then are they to survive? Somewhere on the planet someone wants to buy their products and skills. If only they were aware of all the possibilities and demand, perhaps the peaks, troughs, and periods of zero demand could be evened out to create greater stability.

The Internet might look like an unlikely solution, and yet it is already providing a boon and a life belt for many. Here is a world of chaos, serendipity, and apparent insecurity that is light-years away from the telephone network and yellow pages. How could such a world be of benefit, or even save, any business? Well, the networked world of electronic working defeats both geography and time. Everything can be done much faster, and the limits of geographical separation are minimized.

Until recently, I had to travel to a bookstore to discover they did not have the copy I required. It would then take a month to order what I required and call me to pick up my book from the shop. So I had to wait, make two trips, and pay a high price. Now I buy all my books from virtual bookstores. The Internet bookstores always have the titles I need—at U.S. prices—and dispatch directly to my home in less than two weeks. So I get what I want in a shorter time, at 70 percent of the UK price, and don't have to travel.

A computer company I consult with decided to put all of its sales, marketing, and customer support on the net. Inquires have rocketed to 7000 per week and sales have doubled. Grocery stores, builder supply yards, limousine services, clothing, and office supplies, real estate agents, banks, and many more are currently doing business over the net. In Europe it is the larger businesses and corporations that are dominating this world of electronic commerce. And here is a danger: as stateside companies launch export drives into Europe over the net—at U.S. prices, an invisible market is being built. For those not involved, the mechanism of their demise may remain a total mystery. They may never see what business advantage took away their livelihood. The business world is no longer a village, a city, or a country; it is a planet accessible by computer and modem.

38

"What use could this company make of an electrical toy?"

William Orton, President, Western Union
(rejecting Alexander Graham Bell's offer
to sell his struggling telephone company
to Western Union for $100,000)

IN MY EAR ALL THE TIME

Telecommunication is about shrinking the planet, the removal of geography and barriers. It's not so much: let nation speak unto nation, more let people speak unto people and machines, and let machine speak unto machine. Sitting in my office with the door closed, I only have to call "Mary" and my secretary will kindly respond and be ready to give me help. Similarly, I can call "Brenda" or "Richard" at home, and my wife or son will reply. But when I want to make a telephone call, I have to key in 11 or more digits with my finger and then wait for the electronics to achieve the same objective—a one-to-one connection. When I am in Scotland or America, why can't I just say "Mary" or "Brenda" and have them appear directly in my ear within an instant—or receive an "I'm busy" whisper? I'd also like my computers to respond to my call by name. Can technology do this? I think so. Would people want or like it? Perhaps. Would it pose new threats and problems? Definitely. But so did the telephone in 1876.

Ten years ago I had a voice-activated phone in my car capable of dialing people by name. Today, there are modern versions on the market but without the necessarily discrete headset, memory bank, and speed of processing. So why can't I buy the facility to call anyone I know by name, anytime, or anywhere and save the wear and tear on my eyes, brain, and fingers? The need to remember numbers and frustration of having to wait for access seem out of kilter with much of my IT life. It is probably because no one has thought that it would be a facility we might like. None of this is impossible, and it would not take a lot of engineering. The speech recognition and activation processing can now be accommodated on a single chip for over 100 named people, while the more complex inquiries and access to those we don't regularly call could be dealt with by memory and recognition embedded in the network along with the powerful processing required.

So imagine a future where the 100 most-talked-to people you know are always on tap instantly, by name, and moreover, you are on tap for them. Of course, there may be hundreds more you seldom talk to who can be contacted by name through the network. For these you might accommodate a little more delay for the privilege Would we be able to cope with a no-warning "hello," followed by a direct but ethereal conversation? Would we see a total loss of control of incoming infor-mation and access, get swamped, and be unable to escape? I think not. Although our immediate reaction might be slight panic at the prospect, we already cope with exactly this situation in a world that is not electronic. The world of industry, the crowded room, the open field, sporting event, and home have us all on instant call, always on a the real-life line. Solitude and thought are still possible. We are still in control.

The big difference is, of course, the connection by sight and our most subtle means of communication over a distance, facial expression, gesture, and body language. The telephone is already an intrusive instrument capable of butting into conversations in a way that is not always socially acceptable. Could it just be that our desire for instant communication will see us accepting the ultimate intruder, just a voice in the ear?

39

HUMAN HARMONY AND CHAOS

Just 20 years ago all telephones were on the end of a wire and static, with users making an average of two or three telephone calls per day at unrelated times. True, there were busy hours, mealtimes and coffee breaks would see a distinct lack of calls, but by and large, calls were governed by random events. This all changed with the arrival of TV phone-in programs. Someone singing a song on TV could result in a half million people telephoning Chicago to cast votes for their local hero in the space of 15 minutes. A new world of network chaos was born.

With the arrival of the mobile telephone, a new phase of chaos erupted. Traffic jams and train and plane cancellations all trigger correlated activity; everyone calls home or office within a few minutes. Naturally enough, cellular systems become overloaded as thousands of people demand to be connected at the same time. So a transition has occurred, from a random world of reasonably distributed events to a highly localized and correlated world of activity triggered by anything causing us to act in unison.

Traveling the planet as I do, I have developed a routine to cope with that childlike fear of waking up in the dark and not knowing quite where I am. At 7:00 a.m. every morning my laptop wakes up, and the screen glows to fill the room with a foglike light. As I stagger to the bathroom, it goes on-line, dials my server, logs on, collects my mail, and puts it on the screen ready for my attention as I emerge from the bathroom shaved, showered, and ready to go. A few minutes of typing and dressing has me on my way to breakfast. While I'm eating, my laptop automatically dials in, downloads my mail, and retrieves the next batch. This automated process goes on throughout the day. However, designers of this product obviously knew nothing of networks. This application only activates on the hour or half hour. Why is this a problem? Well, suppose 20 people book into the same hotel with the same software. At 7:00 a.m. and every half-hour thereafter, all 20 could be demanding on-line access, and it is highly unlikely the PBX will have 20 spare lines.

All of this might seem trivial and easy to repair, but consider the prospect of networked computing. When 5 or 10 of us meet, our low-cost NCs will be plugged into the same line or server. At critical times during our discussion, several of us will wish to access information or download to distant colleagues. This will be correlated activity with a vengeance and on a large scale that is difficult to contemplate.

Probably the most famous example of correlated activity between machines was the computerization of the London Stock Market and the Big Bang. Here machines programmed with similar buy and sell algorithms had no delay built in. Shortly after cutting over from human operators to machines, the market went into a synchrony of buy, sell, buy, sell. This is an existence theorem for uncontrolled chaos. It is possible.

Many people equate chaos to randomness, but they are very different. Chaotic systems exhibit patterns that can be in a near-cyclic manner often difficult for us to perceive. Random systems, on the other hand, are totally unpredictable. Curiously, without computers we would know little or nothing about chaos, and yet they may turn out to be the ultimate generators of network chaos on a scale we might not be able to match.

40

*"Man is an over-complicated organism.
If he is doomed to extinction he will
die out for want of simplicity."*

Ezra Pound (1938)

FLYING BLIND

Imagine being told that when you throw a ball, the trajectory will be straight for a distance, followed by an abrupt fall to the ground. You would immediately contest this on the basis of your earliest childhood recollections that the trajectory is actually an arc. Unfortunately, much of our understanding is not based on such an easily assimilated experience, and, for example, we can safely assume no one understands quantum mechanics. The notion that an atom effectively changes size on the basis of the speed of approach of a proton is something we cannot experience directly. But this is well-founded and lies at the heart of calculating the probability of a collision or nuclear fission. The counterintuitive nature of such interactions means only a fraction of the population can cope with atomic physics. Computer simulation and VR now offer new windows into such worlds that surpass all established methods of modeling and visualization. Since the ancient Greeks and until recent times, modeling and understanding has been dominated by difficult-to-comprehend mathematics. It has therefore been inaccessible to all but a few educated in the art of abstract manipulation and hieroglyphic formulation. All this is now changing—fast.

Throughout our formal educations we are fed a diet of problems that can be solved. From our earliest days at school we are led to believe that our world is dominated by well-behaved and understandable phenomena. But it is actually grossly nonlinear and difficult to understand. The stock market, weather prediction, earthquakes, water flow, road traffic, advertising, and crowd behavior are common examples.

So in many respects we have been fortunate in being able to develop the majority of our systems and technologies on nominally linear assumptions. Before the arrival of computers, we saw very strong links between our direct experience, physical models, and mathematics. However, technology has now introduced and opened up new realms that are not coupled to any of our previous experience. For example, the sheer scale of software programs of millions of lines of code, with thousands of loops and decision points, is way beyond raw human brainpower to understand. We are definitely wetware limited.

An analogous, and hugely complex, system would be trying to build a bridge on the basis of the binding energies in the nucleus of the iron atom. This would be fundamentally impossible. And yet the simple abstraction to Young's Modulus of Elasticity allows us to stand back from any deep physical understanding of iron with sufficient accuracy to construct a bridge fit for purpose. The difficulty with software is that we have yet to discover a suitable abstraction. Although we have migrated from machine code to high-level languages, we are still unable to grasp the full picture. Perhaps VR will allow us to enter such realms to gain a new perspective and an understanding of the grossly nonlinear.

As recently as the 13th century, the use of pictures in mathematics was decried, and yet beyond a good left-right brain connect, visualization is probably the single most powerful tool available for understanding the topic. But a parallel situation also exists today with those who decry the use of IT. The reality is that without computers, the world of complexity would remain totally hidden. Chaos and fractals cannot be explored without the screen. Turning the complex into animated, 3D, color, pictographic form gives a new route to understanding. It is almost certain that this technology holds the vital key to creating a generalized understanding of almost everything. Without it, we would know virtually nothing about turbulent flow in gases and fluids, economic systems, human interaction, or evolutionary theory. We would be flying blind.

41

"Art is an experience, not the formulation of a problem."

Lindsay Anderson (1989)

ART AND SCIENCE

For the first time in 400 years or so, it would appear art and science are coming back together. Multimedia, virtual reality, humanized interfaces, and the need to create environments where the understanding of complex and nonlinear situations is both possible and accessible to everyone are primary drivers of this remarriage. No doubt, Michelangelo and Leonardo da Vinci would be amazed at the original divorce, as both were artist and engineer. Galileo on the other hand, was more scientist and engineer. But all three fostered the desire to find the truth, to understand and use the forces and materials of nature to the advantage of humankind. All were also subject to the constraints of the religious oppression of the day and the public fear engendered by witchcraft and alchemy. The truth was what mattered and distinguished scientist and engineer from the forces of religion and art—blind truth against blind belief. The big question now is: Have we grown up sufficiently to live together?

The power of computers is acting as a growing intermediary between many different groups and disciplines. Mathematicians, scientists, engineers, and artists can now talk and understand each other as never before. Even the subgroupings inside science are finding it useful to come together through IT. Computer and network science are encompassing biology and discovering new things in all three disciplines, for example. The computer (our third lobe) and visualization technologies are effecting a very viable left brain-right brain connect.

They are also proving a most powerful tool for rapid mediation and understanding.

In modern management the necessity of being part of a team is promoted heavily. In much of art it would appear that the individual still rules, while in engineering and science, teams have been essential for decades. The lone mathematician can still pursue a solitary course, but for the majority of technologists the team is the closest you can get to true understanding. A group consciousness is necessary to pursue all the facets involved in big problems which extend well beyond the abilities of single minds or disciplines.

It is as if all of human knowledge is a thin layer of ice (understanding) on a vast sea of the unknown, waiting to be discovered. When we are young, we tend to know a lot about nothing; we are specialized and deep. As we get older, we know almost nothing about a vast amount; we tend toward generalism. It is no longer possible to be the complete holistic human. Educated people no longer exist. It is only possible to be partially educated, to know but an increasingly minuscule fraction of what there is to know. But it does not seem to matter. We have given up the glory of the individual for the glory of the group. Individuals still shine, but everyone contributes to the final outcome.

I vividly remember an eminent scientist repelling a group of artists who proclaimed that scientists understood nothing of beauty. If they saw a flower, the artists would paint or draw it to capture its magnificence, where as the scientists would pull it apart and destroy it. They were wrong, of course. Scientists see the inner beauty of the mathematics that dictate the number and form of the petals, the molecular forms that create the colors and scents. None of this is visible to the artists. They are blind, seeing and understanding almost nothing. Well, it is all changing. Artists can now see these invisible worlds for the first time. Ultimately, the big question is: What will they bring to science and engineering? A lot, I suspect.

42

"Progress everywhere today does seem to come so very heavily disguised as Chaos."

Joyce Grenfell (1978)

DUMBER IS SMARTER

You visit a music store, return home, and insert a newly purchased CD into a dumb box, your hi-fi. You press the play button and get instant music. Why should it be any other way? But the next day you visit a computer store. Returning home, you insert your newly purchased CD into a really smart box, your PC. At this point, you may still be struggling to get at the information on the CD some 15 mouse clicks later. Why is something so simple made so difficult? Why do we have to ensure we have the right version for an operating system and anything between 8 and 32 Mbytes of RAM for essentially the same information?

I can buy a cheap camera with a modest level of integrated automation, including exposure, aperture, focusing, and little more. All I do is point and press to get good pictures. Alternatively, I can buy an expensive top-of-the-line camera and find a level of operational difficulty that beggars belief. The same appears to be true of cars, TV, hi-fi, and much more of our technology. Whatever happened to the old engineering principle of KISS—Keep It Simple, Stupid? What are we doing confounding ourselves with unnecessary complexity? Don't we have the paradigm inverted? Why make interfaces so convoluted and painful? Surely spending more money ought to be rewarded by more simplicity, not more complexity.

During the past year I have purchased a large number of CDs from a diverse range of electronic publishing houses. Here, too, the curious inverse law of price and complexity emerges. The cheaper the CD, the easier and more user-friendly the interface. This spans the sublime to the ridiculous, from insert the CD and double click on the icon to read these instructions, load the installer, plus a nightmare of adjustments and complexity. Also, I now seem to spend a lot of time weeding out multiple copies of movie player, simple text, and a growing variety of applications necessary to support every CD I buy. Is it too much to ask for the illusion of simplicity? Remember when turning the volume up or down was just a twist of a knob instead of three or more clicks of a mouse?

Get inside of a CD or a Web site and we are presented with an infinity of variants that detract from their purpose and our ability to concentrate and navigate successfully. Again, it appears that the more money people have to spend, the more complexity they pile in. More graphics and bells and whistles seem to be the rule. When I'm looking for information when I'm trying to work, I don't want an adventure traveling slowly through some interactive theme park or travelogue. I want to get to information and understanding fast.

There is no doubt about it, hypermedia and hypertechnology present us with a major challenge. As a general rule, humans are not hyperspace thinkers. Most of us are outstanding in 2D, pretty good in 3D, poor in 4D, and definitely in trouble at 5D and above. And yet most IT starts with at least 4D, or at least four degrees of freedom. Just a simple car radio now has LW, MW, FM, Tape, CD, RDS, TA, TP, MESSAGE, FFWD, Scan, Search, Memory. Web sites and CDs have time lines, technology themes, historical perspectives, simulations, movies, text, narration, text to speech, hidden doors and clues, plus much more.

In our physical world we walk from 3D room to 3D room and cope. Going from 5D to 5D seems a tall and unnatural order.

43

*"The distance is nothing;
it is only the first step
that is difficult."*

Marquise du Deffand (1763)

ARE WE SO FAR APART?

I was prompted to estimate the distance between people by the increasing number of times I first meet someone, only to discover we have some mutual acquaintance. So, what is the distance between you and me? How long is the acquaintance chain? I reckon it at never more than six. Pick a Mongolian herdsman, a South American Indian, or someone in any city at random, and there will never be more than six people between us. Confine the set to a profession and two is more likely, and in a country it rarely exceeds three. This might seem extraordinary—and counterintuitive, but put it to the test.

On a recent flight my wife sat beside an Indian gentleman who, it turned out, worked for a company I consult with. I only picked one name in that company and it was his manager—distance one. While waiting for breakfast in a U.S. hotel, I met a pharmaceutical specialist who knew someone I had been to a meeting with the day before—distance one. In a swimming pool in southeast Asia I met a man from mainland China with whom I had a mutual acquaintance—distance one.

Could it be that this people distance has an equivalence in the information world? In recent experiments with directories, I discovered that COCHFORE is a unique designation of me in a population of over one million. That is, the first four letters of my name, followed by the first four letters of my street, identify me alone. Perhaps we should not be surprised as we are looking at 26EXP8 (not quite because of language limitations) possibilities. But ignoring the constraints of language, there are sufficient characters to provide a unique address for everyone on the planet. In principle it ought to be a lot easier to find people and information than it actually is. My physical address has 56 characters, my telephone 12, my e-mail 25, home page 38, bank account 22, and so on. Also, I personally have over 30 different addresses, spanning home, office, telephones, fax, computer, banks, passport, medical, insurance, car, etc. But I actually only need one core address of nine characters for everything.

What of documents? Do they have an association distance? For everyone with a computer there is usually a filing system at least three folders deep. So this takes the people-document distance out to 16 or more. Then, of course, there is the content and subject matter relating them in a more complex and tenuous manner. Dogs, hot-dogs, and food, for example. Now we have a real problem, document distances that are potentially enormous.

Soon we will have more things communicating than people, all with addresses. Because a lot of them will be mobile, we cannot associate addressing with physical location. So we need to cut the problem in a different direction, and it would seem logical to start with the most vital and work toward the insignificant. Ideally, we would be able to remember addresses with ease. And it is within our grasp to create hyperspace addressing to get us to our destination in a very short distance. For example: female, XYZ Company, accountant, educated at MIT; or alternatively: a young woman who wrote a *Business Week* article on accounting futures about a year ago. Both routes ought to be sufficient to locate the individual, and the distance is less than six, and computers could do it better than us. Unfortunately, the future of electronic addressing seems to be going in a different direction, with ever-growing strings of meaningless characters. Machines may be our only hope of finding a human-scale solution, provided we get out of the loop, that is.

44

"Why," said the Dodo,
"the best way to explain is to do it."
Lewis Carrol (Alice in Wonderland)

SHAFTS AND ARROWHEADS

If I were to give you an arrowhead and ask you to bind it to the end of a shaft, I would be amazed if you stood bolt upright, held the shaft at eye level, and proceeded to bind the head to one end. I would expect you to sit or crouch and look down on the artifacts and work in a stooped and concentrated manner. If I were to give you a sheet of paper and a pen and ask you to write a note, I would be amazed if you held it at head height, vertical, and proceeded to write. I would expect you to sit down and crouch and write looking down. For various reasons locked into our dim and distant past, we happen to be about 20 percent more efficient when we read and write looking down on a sheet of paper than when we look straight ahead. This being so, we might then be prompted to ask a fundamental question: Why is it we have vertical computer screens?

By merely laying a computer screen flat and looking straight down, we can improve our ability to read, edit and compose between 15 and 20 percent on average. The reason we do not do this is attributable to two principal limiter's—the television paradigm and the keyboard. We have become conditioned to screens being vertical for entertainment and a lot of our information display, and the keyboard just plain gets in the way and makes it difficult to see over the top.

The contrast ratio of print on paper is around 200, the personal computer gives us around 60, and a laptop computer with liquid crystal display is about 30. A personal organizer with black on gray can be as low as 10. There is no doubt about it, paper is wonderful stuff: user-friendly, flexible, and to some extent reusable. It also allows us to see several pages at a time and not be restricted to the single or fractional page format of the computer screen. Spreading out a complete work over a desktop and looking down at the entire entity is a powerful means of enhancing composition and understanding. On the other hand, the screen is wonderfully flexible and a different kind of workplace, but just a metaphor of the desktop. If the two are going to merge and we are to realize the advantages of both, then it is necessary for the desktop to become completely active. It is also necessary to get rid of the keyboard and probably the mouse.

Imagine for a moment a desktop that is active with the definition and contrast ratio of paper, but with the flexibility and intelligence of a computer. For such a workspace the electronic desktop would no longer be a metaphor but a step ahead of the wood veneer and paper we currently enjoy. In experiments with such technology, we not only see a 15 to 20 percent improvement through our innate ability to focus and concentrate better when looking down than looking straight ahead, but an even higher percentage through animation and interaction with documents that are no longer passive. The next significant step for computers in the fixed office might just be large, active, and high-definition desktop screens, voice interaction, and natural hand manipulation of objects. Combine this with a vertical screen for video-conferencing and telepresence and a new environment is born which resonates with our psychology and physiology.

Perhaps the next step will then be back to true objects, animation, and interaction, and away from the unnatural world of text, spread-sheets, and 2D static graphics.

45

"There are ... intangible realities which float near us, formless and without words; realities which no one has thought out, and which are excluded for lack of interpreters."

Natalie Clifford Barney (1962)

BEING THERE

Videoconferencing systems present images of humans of the wrong size and color that become blurred and jerky with movement. They also lack synchronization between speech and lip movement, have voices that do not emanate from the mouth, do not permit eye contact or body language, and do not create the illusion of "being there." This is often compounded by the need for more than one screen and the lack of any shared workspace. We also appear to stare over each other's heads. All of this adds up to an unnatural and sterile workplace that is difficult to relate to. What is difficult to establish is what users will find realistic enough for them to offset their desire to travel. Perhaps it is not unreasonable to suppose that they expect to see at least a "living room standard" TV presentation.

Throughout the development of videoconferencing, bandwidth and distance have been assumed to be expensive. The world has focused on signal compression and coding for networks of relatively poor performance and restricted bandwidth, low utility, and high price. In reality, optical fibre transmission and digital switching have negated these constraints.

A net result of excessive coding is a delay between transmission and reception that is commonly 0.5 s. In a recent video call I spent two hours talking with people in the U.S. At the end of the call I stepped into the corridor and saw someone I knew well. I voiced a greeting and I received an instantaneous response that startled me. I had become conditioned to the delay.

The focus on signal compression has caused human requirements and interface developments to be neglected. This is compounded by the use of standard TV cameras and screens with poor acoustic coupling between locations rarely fit for the purpose. Studying people in real conference facilities reveals a number of requirements to maximize the chances of success. Mimicking these real environments as closely as possible to provide a facsimile—a "virtual" conference room, and as far as possible, humanize the interfaces and workspace is—now feasible. The recent arrival of large-area, high-definition, daylight-bright display systems is the first real breakthrough for decades that might encourage us not to drive and fly everywhere.

We are remarkably sensitive to eye contact, gaze awareness and movement, body language, and sound. There is no better place to observe this than at a cocktail party. Watch people scan for visual contact, early warning, and indicators—friend or foe, supporter or rival. It is all very subtle. Our acoustic performance is more subliminal and no less impressive. Not only can we talk to one person or group and maintain a sensible conversation, but we can scan the room and pick out the voice and words of an individual many feet away. Despite the hubbub of voices, we can often decode the essential nature of what is being said. Machines find this extremely difficult to do, if not impossible.

All of this happens in meetings and conference rooms too. So the question is: Can electronic environments provide these facilities? In a limited way it appears they can. First of all, large screens with suitably placed cameras can create the illusion of eye contact. Steerable microphone and speaker arrays can create acoustic differentiation linked to our head position and eye focus. Not quite the cocktail party, but close. This technology might just steer us away from excessive travel. In my experience the only people who like to travel are those who do not do it. So perhaps the most demanding requirement is the change of mindset required.

46

"I consider that a man's brain originally is like a little empty attic, and you have to stock it with such furniture as you choose"

Sir Arthur Conan Doyle (1887)

THE NC IN THE ATTIC

My childhood had many special places of curiosity and pleasure. In particular, the garden shed, pantry, and attic had their own chaos, order, colors, and smells. For sheer delight the attic was best. What was it about this collection of dust-covered artifacts that delighted me so? Well, it is difficult to define, but certainly a combination of history, belonging, the evoking of lost memories, discovery, and perhaps an element of voyeurism. In the attic you can discover your history and that of your family.

Today, many PCs parallel the attic, with their guardians loath to allow anyone direct access to the hard disc or screen. Until they are in trouble and need help, they guard access with the same diligence they afford their wardrobe or home. However, when deadlines are fast approaching and nothing is working, then the defenses are dropped to give an opportunity for repair. At this point the desire for privacy and security are waived in the interest of survival.

A non-techno-friend recently called me late one evening because his PC was running badly. Apparently, it was sluggish, crashing regularly, and had been extremely unreliable for weeks. Now this person had reached an impasse and could not work, and a deadline was just 10 hours away, the next morning. So I was firmly invited round to his home and given total access and freedom of action. Please, just fix it fast was the plea.

I started to roam the desktop, which resembled a major highway accident site, with wreckage and fallout extending well into the hard disc. What a mess, how did it ever work? Movie files and documents had been placed inside preference folders and other obscure files inside the operating system. Applications had found their way into working folders. Files and objects had been duplicated, with multiple copies in diverse locations. And worse, at a first scan, more than 30 percent of the hard disc appeared to be chaotically occupied by junk.

Sitting with my friend and feeling slightly uncomfortable, I started the cleanup process—junking, erasing filing, renaming, replacing files, folders, and objects. Nothing was safe, and I trashed over 50 Mbytes. The next step was to place all the working files into a folder and collocate all the applications. After an hour I felt ready to run the diagnostic pack, and we took a break for coffee while it did its stuff. An hour later the PC was debugged, defragged, and running sweeter than ever before.

During the cleanup process I had gently asked questions to try and figure out how this PC had got into such a mess, and it became progressively clear that my non-techno-friend had no idea. It was all a complete mystery. A PC was just a magic box that did stuff, and outcomes were often a surprise or shock.

A few days later I opened my laptop and started my routine cull of old files and messages. Perhaps it was the memory of my friends' PC, or the childhood attic, that prompted me to examine my applications and operating system. I started to delete or to place items into a NOT USED folder. Stickies, scrapbook, numerous print drivers, modem scripts, wizards, art folders, voices, acres of fonts, non-English options, and much more were deleted or isolated. Having cleaned out this IT attic, I found the machine booted up and operated faster and suffered fewer spurious delays and lockups. As I continued to progressively delete soft-junk, some applications were trimmed down to 30 percent of their original size, and I realized I might have found a network computer in the attic.

47

*"With that (computing) science,
we are entering an era of exhaustivity,
which is also an era of exhaustion."*

Jean Baudrillard (1987)

WHO WRITES THE SOFTWARE?

The expansion in software size and complexity is now overtaking the remarkable advances in computer hardware speed and storage density. A sustained doubling of hardware capabilities every 12 to 18 months since 1960 seems no match for applications that required 0.5 Mbytes of RAM 10 years ago and now demand well over 16 Mbytes. So today, we have Power PCs apparently running slower than a 386 of only a few years ago. What is happening? Has the software industry lost control? Will it continue to just consume all future hardware gains, ignore optimization, and provide evermore complex and unwanted facilities embedded in more and more lines of code?

At the present rate of software expansion, we will soon need a supercomputer to write an office memo. And it is not just PC-related software, it is almost universally true of all commercial, defense, and engineering systems. Software just keeps expanding. It is as if we have learned nothing from our decades of working with hardware. Superficially, the engineering differences between hardware and software now seem minimal, and the cost of software manufacture is often greater. So why do we not optimize and worry about software cost and efficiency?

Could it be that software is something so new and complex that it will defy all our efforts at analysis and formalism? Or is it just that we never before had problems with hundreds and thousands of loops and I/O functions. If this is the case, we could be in a new realm of the unknowable, well beyond our mental capacity to decode. So what are we to do? Of course, we can continue on our present course and suffer a continuing and probably terminal slow-down. Alternatively, we can pin our hopes on new programming languages such as Java that are tighter, smarter, and better organized. Perhaps these will lead us to take the vital step to software building blocks that can be glued together in an understandable and efficient manner.

In the physical world, we built bridges of wood and stone and steel, investigated the material properties, and later discovered molecules and atoms. In the software world, we seem to have started with the electrons and have yet to discover molecules, let alone the concept of wood, stone, and steel. We currently lack any suitable abstractions to form a systematic view, and we know nothing of the general properties. Software modules, discrete building blocks, might be the fix we need. However, progress in this direction has been very slow, and there may be a new alternative.

Developments in artificial life systems now see genetic mutation and exchange creating a different richness of solutions. Software that writes itself similarly to the evolutionary process of life is now a crude reality. Control systems requiring millions of lines of code have been replaced by less than a thousand evolutionary lines, and purists now worry about not understanding the way the machines do it. But the truth is we are not particularly clever about understanding how we do it either; the complexity is generally well beyond a single human mind. So here is a new world of machine-generated code, in which they program and learn, and we unknowingly use the tools produced. Most impressively, the machines may soon watch us and learn from our habits as they change and continually modify the code to meet our requirements—a society of new minds perhaps.

For the most part, people do not understand people, and people do not understand machines. The big question is: Will machines understand machines and people? I hope so, it would be a great breakthrough to get some understanding into software.

48

*"People will soon
get tired of staring
at a plywood box
every night."*

D. F. Zanuck, 20th Century Fox (1946)

VIRTUAL TV

Apart from the addition of more scanning lines, color, and a larger screen size, television has changed little since the 1930s. It remains dominated by the cathode ray tube and is a limited and largely passive two-dimensional medium. For a true technological leap forward, we have to go well beyond the current industry desire to sell us higher definition (even more lines); bigger, wider screens; and more channels.

We are moving toward a world of everything on demand: information, interaction, and experience, through visual and acoustic immersion. TV technology can deliver much of this to the home and office by coalescing computers and communications. In a first step in this direction, we are seeing video-on-demand services being tested in trials worldwide. Here, the viewer could ultimately have access to all the video material imaginable, extending to shopping, museums, art galleries, libraries, medicine, care, education—into the complete world of information.

For any chance of success, it is essential that the user interface surpasse the dreaded VHS controller, or for that matter the PC. If this is not the case, we shall see a high proportion of the population effectively frozen out of this information future. Making information available to anyone aged between 3 and 90 is the great challenge; the technology has to be humanized. The way this is being addressed has already moved beyond the graphical user interface (GUI) to the shopping mall, street, store, or library paradigm. Here, the user moves into familiar surroundings, with information access framed as a real, rather than

97

artificial, electronic book; a furniture store instead of a catalogue; a travel agent instead of a brochure. In such an environment you have nothing to learn. All is familiar and intuitive.

Beyond the interface we will be confronted by a vast choice, with thousands of virtual shops and stores across the planet. Selecting a program from a choice of a few tens of channels is manageable. A few hundreds becomes difficult, and 10,000 is impossible. This can be overcome with artificial intelligence primed to learn our changing interest profile. Such a system could even provide a degree of serendipity as it learns about us and offers opportunities to see this or that film, or purchase this or that watch, tie, dress, shirt, tie, etc. An electronically generated short-form preview—the essence of the film, or opportunity, compressed into a few minutes—is already possible.

For a significant step beyond all of this, we have to move to immersive systems, with a large (wall-size) flat panel and head-or-eye mounted displays—a saturation of the visual, acoustic, and ultimately the tactile to realize total interaction. With such technology we will no longer be spectators but participants, part of the feature film, totally involved. This might seem farfetched, but there is nothing here that has not already been tried in research laboratories today.

A more immediate and available technology employs miniature TV cameras mounted at eye level, with microphones above the ears—a surrogate head. The output of this device can be coupled to a VR headset. So if you wear the VR headset and I the surrogate head, then you effectively stand inside me looking out. What I see, you see, what I hear, you hear, and soon, what I feel, you will feel. Why be limited to two people when we can broadcast to millions? In the 21st century perhaps we will all go to the Olympic Games without leaving home, and we may stop watching and start participating.

49

*"It's like driving a car at night.
You never see further than your
headlights, but you can make
the whole trip that way."*

E. L. Doctorow (1988)

CONTENT BREEDS CONTENT

Human progress is critically dependent on each generation's ability to stand on the creative shoulders of those before. Throwing rocks at prey gave way to the spear, the bow and arrow, and ultimately guns. But on the way we invented the lathe, milling machine, and grinder to spin off even more inventions and products. The process of protection through patents came late in the day and served to promote rather than stem the inventive stream and progress. And so the thermionic valve gave way to the transistor, integrated circuit, and the vast array of new technologies we enjoy today.

Intellectual property is also protected by copyright, which was originally concerned with authorship and prose. This ancient paradigm has now moved into the world of software and is both an impediment to progress and the subject of confusion. It seems reasonable that a book should be protected against plagiarism and banditry, but software is different. Here we have an interactive and creative space where elements can be mapped from one system or function to another. No one would consider making individual nuts and bolts anymore; we just buy them by the box. Well, software is available in boxes too, but it comes with a copyright restriction. This often means no copying or modification under any circumstances, and almost certainly no access to the source code.

The same is true of content. From music to video and animation, copyright now serves to restrict rather than promote use, and worse, to stem invention. The old world was about producing a few things and selling them at high prices. The new is enabling the converse, selling very large numbers at very low prices. It is about assembling readily available and networked components, adding new and original material, and rapidly advancing the art. Copyright is stemming this positive feedback process that served the progress of hardware so well. In effect, software copyright often means having to make every nut, bolt, and screw as if they could not be replicated or mass produced.

Ideally, a new regime is needed, a fresh approach that is neither copyright nor patent in the old sense, something that can deal with a networked world where copying is so tempting and easy and effective policing almost impossible. In the past, copyright made everyone criminals by default as they recorded radio and TV material off the air. Now people are tempted by the sharing of games, applications, and programs. For sure, a human software police force and teams of lawyers are not the solution, but electronic agents and operating bombs might be. Attaching agents to software that flag intrusion, modification, and use to the originator are simple to realize in a networked world. The firewall of the floppy, CD, and snailmail may only require the inclusion of warning flags and by-use self-destruct or corrupting mechanisms.

Ultimately, the solution may fall solely with the originators and users of code and may not require the attention of outside agencies. Technology has now reached a point where it can take care of itself without human intervention. Our interests would be best served if we concentrated on encouraging the propagation and use of software to create an increasingly rich and growing field of content. Software and content could then beget even more, since positive feedback would take full reign. The old and outmoded quill pen copyright mentality will only serve to restrict the fundamental mechanisms of progress—standing on the shoulders of others. As my old university professor once observed: Borrowing one man's results is plagiarism, but borrowing from ten is research.

50

*"The idea that information can be
stored in the changing world
without an overwhelming
depreciation of its value is false."*

Norbert Wiener (1950)

DIGITAL ILLUSIONS

The benefits of going digital are manifest in the infinite varieties, malleability, reproducibility, transmission switching, routing, and storage potential of all forms of data. In theory, once we have captured text, images, movies, sound files, simulations, and models, they can be stored forever without degradation of the original form, and can be copied or transmitted anywhere free from distortion. These, then, are the key differentiators from the earlier and far more volatile world of analogue information. But there is also a hidden facet, and that is the economic benefit which came with the ability to manufacture the transistor and integrated circuit. Even though it requires far greater complexity, realizing almost anything in digital form is generally far lower in cost than analogue in terms of repeatability and mass production. All of this was apparent in the early 1960s when the digital revolution began, and it more or less remains the case today. So we have a digital telephone network, LANs, Internet, copper, optical fiber, radio, and satellites transporting information across the planet in an almost seamless fashion. For real-time speech and moving pictures any bit loss is managed down to a point where it is imperceptible. For financial and other data great care is taken to ensure a zero-bit-error transfer. All this works and is accepted, and the digital world now dominates.

Why, then, do I find a slow degradation of images and other digitally stored material? What is going wrong? It appears that uncontrolled and unseen transformations now pose a threat. At the simplest level, just try and access digitally stored documents from 10 years ago. First, the original application may have disappeared or have been replaced by something more advanced that will not read your document or changes the format of the data. Second, the reader hardware may be in a museum, or you may not have the correct fonts, characters, lines, and color pallet, but the data might still be there and ultimately accessible. More difficult is the storage disc that has been corrupted by stray fields, read-write errors, or just natural magnetic decay. Floppy and hard discs are far from perfect, and they do deteriorate with time.

On a more subtle and unseen level, we have digital format transformations where information is destroyed and lost forever. This can be as rudimentary as formatting information between applications. Image processing is a prime example, with bit mapping to and from a limited choice color pallet and definition. Once an image has changed down from thousands of colors to 256, from 32 to 16 bits, and so on, there is no way back, information has been lost forever. Cascade through several digital transforms and the damage is usually all too obvious.

Coding presents a more subtle mechanism for information loss. Squeezing data into ever-tighter storage spaces and narrower transmission channels can produce a progressive distortion that becomes amplified by repeated concatenation of such lossy processes. It is often the case that zero-loss coding processes are only "almost zero" in reality. In a fast-moving world of technology, advances in coding algorithms now parallel those in applications. If you repeatedly move your information between machines, applications, and operating systems, don't be surprised at a fading digital illusion.

Perhaps we should not be surprised by this outcome of our digital technology. Somewhere on the planet there will be a virgin copy of what we lose or corrupt, a bit like the printing plate held by the Royal Mint so the currency in our pockets can be updated. For now, however, I'm putting my trust in a CD burner.

51

"Men are only as good as their technical development allows them to be."

George Orwell (1940)

REBOOT TRIGGERS

At a recent air show, I observed a young man sitting in the cockpit of a modern fighter aircraft excitedly talking to the pilot about the design, performance, and instrumentation. The pilot seemed impressed by the knowledge this potential protégé had gained through flight simulation packages. Soon they moved onto the weapons system and the clutch of buttons and triggers clustered on the head of the joy stick. To the young man's surprise, there was an extra trigger for no obvious purpose. The pilot revealed it to be the software reboot trigger. Yep, they actually reboot software mid-flight, during battle, and sometimes more than once.

So here was a $40M machine with flaky software. I tried to get more detail and was told that it was not uncommon and did not constitute a primary risk or degrade the machine's flying ability. But I couldn't help wondering about other defense systems, civil aircraft, nuclear reactors, and my car. Yes, my PC can lock up from time to time, but please, not my engine management system. I already have a car hi-fi with a mind of its own and no reboot mechanism. The garage is trying its best to fix it, but the only way to reboot is to disconnect the battery. Soon, I shall resort to cutting into the wiring harness to install a trigger on my gearshift. Come to think of it, perhaps that is what those pilots did.

Looking back to my childhood, I recall when most technology was unreliable: the radio, TV, record player, cameras, clocks, wristwatch, and electricity supply—in fact, everything was flaky. Driving a car 50 miles was a major expedition, and switching the radio on was a bit chancy too. All of these technologies have now changed to become phenomenally reliable, but it has taken over 100 years of commercial development, competitive markets, and consumer pressure to achieve. Mechanical, electromechanical, electrical, electronic, and production engineering have come a very long way, as have the design and man-ufacturing process. More notably, our requirements for quality in everyday technology have also risen dramatically. We now demand it.

In contrast, popular software for the masses has only been around for a couple of decades, and as an industry it lacks any real competi-tion. Packages tend to be unique, noninteroperable and noninter-changeable, and there are no common operating platforms or systems. Moreover, software continues to be developed at a pace that keeps us dazzled by the diversity and abundance. Although this new tool and medium is vital to our future progress and prosperity, it is generally unstable and likely to remain so for at least another decade.

Among some classes of software and systems, however, there are signs of a growing stability. Watches, calculators, pagers, mobile phones, washing machines, dishwashers, and other small contained systems have perhaps come to the end of an evolutionary road and are stable. Thankfully, engine management, TV, and hi-fi systems are also in this category. But large systems like the PC present major difficul-ties. Loading new applications and upgrading software still makes you hold your breath. When will this situation change? Only when there is sufficient competition, uniformity, compatibility, and we complain enough and have the option to vote with our feet.

Network computing might just be the opportunity we need to bring about the necessary change. A universal operating system and lan-guage with an effective infinity of vendors may be on the horizon. Then we might get a universal and basic word processor, graphics package, spreadsheet, mail, plug and play, and much more—all of it honed up and nonflaky, with no reboot triggers.

52

"Time is a waste of money."
Oscar Wilde (1894)

THE DELAY IN DELAY

Only 15 years ago, using computers and making telephone calls was something of an ordeal. The processing speed of computers and printers meant you could wait for seconds or minutes for screen fill or printout. For telephone users the concatenated electromechanical switching delays meant you could wait over 30 seconds after dialing the last digit (remember those old mechanical dials?) before you heard any ring or engaged tone. How different today. Now we get irritated if we do not hear the ring tone as soon as we press the last digit on the keypad, or when we have to wait seconds for a PC application to load. The generic problem is having to wait for a period that is too short to do anything else but long enough to break our concentration. Delays of a fraction of a second disrupt our mental agility and interactive creativity to an alarming degree.

In contrast, with optical fiber and power PCs, we now have an abundance of bandwidth, storage capacity, and processing power. Moreover, technology promises even higher levels of circuit density and clock speed at insignificant cost. We are thus approaching the realization of a dream: to access everything, everywhere, anytime within three clicks of a mouse and have screen fill and interaction within a second. For us to enjoy natural and effective communication with people and machines, in real or virtual worlds, the need is for sensory delays of less than 100 ms.

Why foster such a dream? The principal reasons are twofold. First, we live in an accelerating world where we all have to do more in less time, and delays limit our creativity and output. Second, it can be done. Trying to interact with anything or anyone at less than natural human speed is counterproductive and irritating. Try a telephone call over a geostationary satellite, which introduces over 300 ms of delay, and it is obvious. An even more obvious experience is that of trying to access information from the Internet—the Information Super Cart Track. Here, delay is endemic due to inappropriate protocols and layers of unnecessary and inefficient software. Even writing a letter, sending e-mail, and manipulating simple documents now seems to require a power PC to get delays down to a few seconds. The reality is that many applications waste increasing MBytes of RAM making the front end prettier and providing unwanted and unused facilities, rather than making the process more slick and effective.

Deregulated telecommunications markets may soon see the concatenation of digital mobile telephones (with an internal codec delay in excess of 120 ms), statistical multiplexers, ATM switches, and satellite, and cable links of numerous uncoordinated suppliers adding undefined transmission delays. This new regime of unpredictable delays will take us further away from realizing another dream: matching person and machine to achieve effective and efficient communication and creativity. But perhaps most dangerous is the prospect of economic routings chosen in ignorance of the final application. E-mail is never a problem, but speech with a total coding and transmission delay of more than 0.5 s would be a disaster.

Just watch children interact with machines and it is immediately apparent that they have an insatiable desire for instant gratification—the shortest response time and best graphics. Looking at professionals you see the same phenomena—a desire to be able to do more faster. All the technology required is available today; we only have to adopt the right mindset and implement the solutions. In the meantime, I suspect our progress will continue to be frustrated by the delays of systems, computers, and software configured for the past.

53

*"Tralfamadorians, of course, say that
every creature and planet in the
Universe is a machine. It amuses them
that so many Earthlings are offended
by the idea of being machines."*

Kurt Vonnegut (StarTrek)

SILICON LIFE

Self-organization and chaos are vital ingredients for all carbon-based life. Every living thing exists on the edge of a
strange attractor, just a hair's breadth from death, in a risky,
fit-for-purpose, nonlinear world of weak hierarchies, a world
where simple rules predicate complex behavior. Here, uncertainty, competition, mutation, and reproduction are key to
survival and progress. Unless life lives on the edge, it does not
live at all. So far, these principles have not been applied to
engineered systems which are largely linear, optimized,
strongly hierarchical, noncompetitive, and minimize risk
through large safety margins and free energy.

It is curious that we are moving in a direction of creating
evermore complex software to perform essentially simple tasks. In contrast,
nature does the converse, generating unbelievably complex behavior from
incredibly simple software. The difference, of course, is the millions of years
nature has been allowed to get it right. We, on the other hand, face much
shorter time scales. But simple life systems like worms, ants, and bees have
been simulated on modest computers realizing the major interactions in
nests and communities. Some of this work has now moved to practical
application as control software for networks and information agents.

While the underlying software for each entity may be only a few
hundred lines of easily understood code, the emergent behavior of a
society of such entities is another matter. This generally defies prediction
and is full of surprises. It might just be that systems of this type cannot

be engineered from the standpoint of our established methods and principles. We may have to let go of our long-held desire to define and constrain all the outcomes by specifying, designing, and testing systems.

Exponentially growing communication, mobility, and information working is creating an increasingly chaotic world. The notion that everything can be controlled, ordered, and specified in a manner reminiscent of the early days of the telephone is a grave error. No matter how many people are employed, there will never be enough. Systems will not be able to keep up with the developments of applications, peripheral devices, and new modes of human-machine interdiction.

Taking a leaf out of nature's book, it is clear that we will increasingly need evolutionary systems to meet chaotic demand. Genetics, sex, mutation, and progeny spring to mind, but we cannot afford to wait for millions of years of chance mutation. Looking at carbon systems, we see a world dominated by one- and two-sex systems. Two sexes are the most adaptable, complex, and intelligent. So we might suppose that sex in software, with the super speed of machines, might suffice. But should we be constrained by nature as to the mechanism and numbers involved, or, indeed, the nature of the progeny? Probably not. In software there are no constraints whatsoever. Morality and society do not exist to constrain the riches of behavior.

We might envisage a silicon world where a learned and positive behavior is passed on from one generation to another. Progeny by installments might be a new means of avoiding the evolutionary cul-de-sacs that hamper carbon. When you have evolved to become an elephant, you cannot backtrack to become a mouse, no matter how many generations you wait. Progeny by piece parts, many offspring glued together to make the whole, may then provide a solution.

When all of this comes together with noisy decision making, a subtle blending of random uncertainty and chaos, instead of the full determinism of nailed down logic and software, we may have the right conditions for silicon life. The question is: Are we smart enough to spot artificial life when it spontaneously erupts?

54

"Do not be bullied by authoritative pronouncements about what machines will never do. Such statements are based on pride, not fact."

Marvin Minsky, MIT (1982)

DONOR CARDS FOR ROBOTS

For some years, top-of-the-line copiers and other office machinery have had enough built-in intelligence to call for maintenance help through a self-dial telephone call. Such intelligence is now being extended to the garage forecourt for the replenishment of fuel, detection of spillages, and maintenance of pumping equipment. Automatic calls for replenishment of food- and commodity-dispensing machines at airports, stations, and in the main street is a more recent development. The logistical advantages of this technology are subtle and significant. Only visiting sites when necessary saves time, resources, and money, but topping off machines in response to exceptional demand means sales opportunities are not missed. Drink machines sell more when it is hot and are soon emptied by local events that are hard to predict, such as flight and train delays and traffic jams. In the not-too-distant-future we might expect this capability to be an integral part of homes, appliances, cars, and body-worn devices.

Most of us already wear a remarkable range of electronics in the form of watches, pagers, calculators, and mobile phones. The office we wear that integrates all of these functions with computing power may not be so far away, and with it will come the added bonus of remote health monitoring in real time.

In the West today, some 2 percent of the population are diabetic, and even more are on some form of drug treatment. Ideally, these people should get constant monitoring and care to meet their needs, which represents a significant work load for the health care system. As technology extends our longevity and the birth rate declines, we face a future of increasing numbers of dependent people and a diminishing number of careers. In the 21st century, providing the level of care that we enjoy today will be inconceivable. We will have an older population and far fewer people working and creating wealth, so some new technological solutions will be necessary.

With a future of wearable electronics, it is feasible that the fundamental monitoring of heart, respiration, blood pressure, skin, salinity, blood glucose, and other characteristics can be provided in real time. Such features could become a part of the office you wear, coupled to algorithms that maintain the right balance of insulin through an artificial pancreas or drug balance through automatic dispensers. But it does not stop here. What about the technology that wears us? The number of internal body part replacements is accelerating, and they are increasingly electronic or mechatronic in form. It is inconceivable that we should give copying machines the intelligence to call for help when they are about to fail and then neglect the pacemaker or artificial heart on which so many people are dependent for their very existence.

In the research laboratories of the world there are already prototype artificial replacements for the pancreas, the liver, the kidneys, the inner ear, and other vital organs. So we are faced with the prospect of larger numbers of people becoming a little less human and a little more cyborg. In the ultimate analysis my 7-year-old son spotted the really obvious. Today, we have donor cards for all real human tissue parts replacement. Being hit by a bus or suddenly dying from whatever cause means that you and I can leave vital organs for the immediate use of disadvantaged people who are still alive. The logical extension is that we need a donor card so that our artificial heart, kidneys, or other replacement parts may also be recovered and used by others. The ultimate extrapolation really is donor cards for robots.

55

WHAT'S SEX GOT TO DO WITH IT?

Of all the life forms on planet earth, only homo sapien optimizes anything. Buy a compact car and it may not be optimized for speed, but it will be reliable. Buy a racing car and you get the speed, but then you have to worry about reliability. The fact that optimization, brittleness, and reliability go hand in hand is something we learned over thousands of years and now use to great effect. Being able to make reliable and low-cost products is a key plank of our society. In contrast, mother nature only employs fit-for-purpose. She optimizes nothing, and her survival statistics are often very impressive. So, have we missed an engineering trick?

Reliability and reproducibility are key achievements of the industrial age, realized through incremental improvements from one generation to the next. This is a powerful and directed evolutionary process where we stand on the shoulders of previous generations and employ cumulative experience and knowledge. It is unlike any mechanism found in nature and results from hierarchical and structured thinking. Modular design and construction definitely works. If you can make a lathe from a bow and arrow, then you can make a better one with the parts you produce. Similarly, if you can make transistors, you can make circuits, and then integrated circuits, and then machines that make better transistors. And so positive feedback accelerates the process as machines beget better machines. Mother nature never uses such directed evolution because it requires intelligence—and a godlike hand.

So what of future software systems; can we expect new engineering processes to emerge? You might think so, but perhaps not, since the majority of human thinking is tempered by direct experience of things physical. Also, our limited ability to access nonphysical experience might be a key constraint. Just how do you understand two million lines of high-level and very abstract code? Our mathematical tools and thinking are useless for systems of such scale and complexity, and so we resort to modular designs, precluding optimization and directed evolution. All of this leads to slow response times and poor reliability.

Mother nature understands nothing and so would not do it this way. She would use blind evolution through natural selection and chance mutation over millions of years. But we cannot afford such development times; we need solutions in weeks. Fortunately, the speed of machines allows us to accelerate the evolution of software entities, so a million years takes less than a week. In carbon life it is the single-sex systems that dominate (flora and fauna), two-sex systems that are the smartest (mammals), and the multiple-sex systems that enjoy the better resilience (insects and fungi). To be really smart also seems to entail enhanced attraction through the mechanisms inherent in sexual reproduction. In software love has nothing to do with the process. It is cold and calculated, with the same regard for survival of the fittest seen in the insect and plant worlds. But there is now a new card to play. Software can adapt and adopt the right number of sexes to meet the needs of a particular problem. Interestingly, the smartest software evolved to date seems to come from four sexes, not two.

So when we try to predict the future, we should remember the lathe and the transistor and contemplate the feedback impact of rapidly evolving software. Machine intelligence will speed up the process further and will not be hampered by emotion, or for that matter, the mating incompatibilities and sexual limitations of carbon life. But like us, future machines will be concerned with information and disorder processing. Only they will be faster and better at it.

56

MORE OUT THAN IN

Just what is it that constitutes true intelligence? What is it that apparently elevates us above machines, and perhaps all living things? To date, we have no formal definition for intelligence that is universally accepted, tried, and proven. Estimating the intelligence of systems has us resorting to crude computations of neural count, processing speed, and connectivity. So we as a species have around 10EXP11 neurons and a 10EXP4 connectivity. Given the uncertainties in getting the numbers right in the first place, that is, counting the numbers per unit volume of brain, puts *us* in the 10EXP15 bracket. Now, include our synaptic processing rate of around 10–100 bits/s and some localization assumptions, and we look like a 1 TFlop/s processor. But we know we are much more.

Chances are that our current estimates of our brain capacity are grossly on the low side, if for no other reason than that we do not fully understand how our own wetware functions. One obvious factor that does distinguish us from silicon machines is our relative information I/O rate. For us, information flow is strictly dominated by input rather than output. From the moment we are born until we die, our sensory systems are feeding our brains vast amounts of information. Our utterances and animation pall into insignificance in raw bit-rate terms, compared to the visual, audio, and tactile input we constantly absorb.

As best we can estimate, each of our eyes feeds us bits from 127,000,000 rods and cones in the retina, via the visual cortex, at about

1 Gbit/s. This far outweighs the infeed from our hearing, tactile, smell, and taste sensors, which total less than 20 Mbit/s. In contrast, our typing rate is only around 40 bits/s, speech is about 100 bit/s, while gesticulation and facial expression are even lower, but of course can be socially encoded to cover far more. A glance from a loved one at a cocktail party or a close colleague in a meeting can be worth Mbits.

Contrast all of this with the average PC, or better still, the mainframe. We complain about them being dumb machines, and yet we deprive them of input. For the most part, all they get is a diet of low bit-rate alphanumerics, no direct visual and audio feed and certainly no tactile, taste or smell. So they all seem to operate in the mode of creating more output than input. From billing customers to issuing pay slips, predicting the weather, or controlling a space shot, their input is meager compared to their output. No wonder they are dumb.

For machines to achieve true intelligence might then require a change of I/O bias. I suspect they will need much more input data, more contemplation processing time, and less time and resources devoted to output. Of all the human kind we revere, it is probably the thinkers who make the greatest impact on human progress. Often they are accused on being noncommunicative, but perhaps that is the secret. Deep thought demands concentration and a degree of mental isolation. Input dominates in all such cases, but when the output comes, it can be momentous, like $E = mc^2$, for example.

We have within our grasp the basic technologies to build machines that might just be capable of some form of free thinking. What is lacking is a suitably formatted information infeed, a sensory system that will match them into our world and others. Perhaps that is why one famous machine of science fiction came to the conclusion that the answer to an important human question was 42, which is 101010, just a free-running clock.

57

*"640K ought to be
enough for anybody."*

Bill Gates (1981)

THANKS FOR THE MEMORY

Just 14 years ago my PC had 1 MByte of RAM and 20 MBytes of disk storage. My word processing package required less than 0.5 MByte of RAM, and my document store oscillated around 3 MBytes. In fact, most applications at that time, and there were few, consumed somewhere between 0.35 and 0.5 MBytes of RAM. What a contrast today. A top-end word processing package requires at least 8 MBytes and can demand as much as 32 MBytes. The same is true of spreadsheet, graphics, and animation applications. Moreover, there is an increasing need to have several of these heavyweight applications running at the same time. As I type these 12 words, I not only have a word processing application open, but a spreadsheet, graphics package, diary application, mail system, and a raft of on-line connections. My computer now has 10 GBytes of hard disk and 500 MBytes of RAM. In the same 14-year period, the clock speed has gone from a mere 6 to 320 MHz, and curiously, the word processor is more sluggish. What have we done?

It is interesting to plot the progress of hardware and software operating speeds and our own perceptions. While computer hardware platforms are increasingly powerful, roughly doubling in capability every 12 to 18 months, the software industry's race to build the world's heaviest airplane, is causing the overall performance to get worse. At the present rate of progress, we will require a Cray Super Computer to write a simple office memo by the year 2015. Clearly, this trend is not sustainable; it cannot continue. Surely word processing, spreadsheet, and graphic packages must have come to the end of the road in terms of their demand for more memory.

From a user point of view, we see a tidal wave of new facilities and extensions. Not surprisingly, we now find it increasingly difficult to operate and exploit applications much beyond a few percent of their full capability. There are no longer any experts. We are all amateurs discovering day by day new quirks and features. Our difficulties are further compounded by cosmetic changes that shuffle the location of commands and the appearance of menus and icons between subsequent versions. On top of all this, there are backward and forward compatibility limitations between releases that provide another layer of frustration.

What is going to be interesting in the next few years is the emergence of distributed computing with Applets on demand. Given the constraints of the present telecommunications network, this will automatically dictate that we scroll back to applications of just a few hundred kBytes when on-line access is required. If we do not, the delays encountered in pulling these down the line will be enormous and will stifle the creation of a world of distributed working. It might be that an alternative world will also emerge in which the producers of software sell us a basic word processing package and then we choose to purchase those features that we really need rather than buying all of it. Suddenly, we would then become the masters of our own destinies and the constructors of our own applications in a Legolike software world.

So, will we still need a large amount of RAM and hard disc storage? Very probably. The reasons: The hardware manufacturers will seek to maintain and/or expand their turnover, coupled with falling hardware costs. But probably the key driver will be ourselves and our desire to own and hold onto software. We are also moving in a direction of having at least five applications open simultaneously in order to complete increasingly complex tasks. So unless someone starts to integrate the Applets for word processing, graphics, spreadsheet, e-mail, and the like, we will remain MByte hungry.

58

"Stocks have reached what looks like a permanently high plateau."

Irving Fisher, Yale University (1929)

THE INFINITE CITY

Only a dozen years ago just over 170 individual dealing rooms employed thousands in the city of London. Eye contact, face-to-face interaction, telephones, and paper were the medium. Few could envisage the death of this system until the big bang of October 1986. The liberalization of the market and global computer-based trading left the floors deserted. Screen trading was a revolution that changed the nature of money markets forever. The first lesson of the big bang was predicted by many with just a modest appreciation of system dynamics. Delay and synchronization in similarly distributed systems rapidly forces them into limit cycles as delay is diminished. In nontechnical terms: Trading systems go into a chaotic buy, sell, buy pattern, and delay had to be put back in to restore stability.

In 1986 Ph.D.s were rare in the city of London, but today dealing systems have become rocket science. The reason: Whoever has the best communications, computers, and algorithms has the edge. Despite all their apparent sophistication, the majority of human traders use a decision process that is simple, and amazingly successful. As shares go up, they assume they will continue to go up until they turn down, and then continue to go down until they turn back up again. Couple this with knowledge and intuition and you have a world-class trader. Computers with algorithms based on this approach are relatively successful and make money, but they need more intelligence to compete.

Today's leading-edge systems use artificial intelligence to buy and sell across global markets. These algorithms learn from experience and predict what should happen, analyze the results, and adjust to improve. In reality, these are simple animals, but then simple animals, such as ants, are able to achieve remarkable things that humans find impossible. So we may soon see traders being replaced by computers guided by very few people. So far, machines don't commit crimes, rarely make mistakes, are nonemotional, and are truly objective. They can work 24 hours a day, 365 days a year, and are totally dedicated. So what might be the next step for the already metaphoric city? Perhaps screen-based trading rooms will also become museums.

If we are working from screens, we don't have to be in one room—or be a part of the same company. As in many other sectors, working from home or telecommuting is an obvious next step and signals the fragmentation of the industry. To realize such freedom requires us to recognize that we are now witnessing the death of geography, the birth of universal information access, and worldwide round-the-clock working. Instant communication compresses distance and eradicates time zones. Why do London, Frankfurt, New York, and Tokyo all have stock exchanges? In an electronic world they will just be information space, without physical location—the infinite city.

Moving from the trading floor to the electronic dealing room saw a phenomenal shrinkage in people numbers and change in the skills required. In the next phase it will be the hybrids, of technologist, banker, marketeer, and trader, who will lead. And the ultimate question: How clever will we have to be to outstrip automatic trading systems in 20 years time? Probably more intelligent than our wetware (brain) allows. What we perceive as random is often chaotic, and chaotic events have patterns which we are good at spotting. This is the basis of human trading systems. The machines' advantage is their ability to take a wider perspective, recognize short-term patterns faster, and continuously examine the outcomes of all previous moves. In short, they are smarter than we are.

59

"I don't want to achieve immortality through my work, I want to achieve it by not dying."

Woody Allen (1975)

DO WE HAVE TO DIE 100 PERCENT?

For millennia all our knowledge could easily be contained in one human brain. Father would teach son, mother would teach daughter, each generation adding a little more. It then became necessary to record information on cave walls, clay tablets, skins, and parchment. We had reached a critical epoch; all human knowledge could no longer be contained in one brain. Specialization and cooperation were vital. No individual could do everything, compete, and survive.

Today, our problem is acute. It is no longer possible to be an expert in anything other than a few virginal topics. For example, just 500 years ago, it was possible to be an expert artist, engineer, and scientist at the same time. Even 30 years ago, it was possible to have a detailed understanding of telecommunication networks, cars, domestic appliances, and military systems. Who now understands all of it? No one. Fortunately, we do not have to understand the chemistry of a safety match to use one—but someone somewhere does.

Despite specialization and an exponential growth in knowledge, we still see people of outstanding ability able to understand and contribute more than average. Unfortunately, they die and their expertise is lost for all time. The question is: Can we capture their expertise and presence for future generations? Do they have to die 100 percent?

Multimedia holds out the prospect of being able to capture such wisdom with the spoken and printed word, supported by animated pictures. Suppose as some great teacher gave lectures and interacted one-on-one with students, it was record-ed. Over a period of years, it is feasible to capture over 95 percent of all likely questions and debate. How difficult, then, would it be to con-struct an artificial persona of this great mind? Might we sit and listen and watch a lecture long after the professor's death and still be able to interact in a meaningful way?

This vision is partially available with today's crude CDs of a mere 630 MBytes capacity, soon to be replaced by the next generation at 8 GBytes. We can already visit the Natural History Museum and receive a description of Barionix or the derivation of the word *dinosaur*. Granted, the presentation and style are limited by the medium, but it is a first indication of what might be done. Our rudimentary artificial intelligence systems can now filter and assemble the right slices of dia-logue. Animation and pictographic representations on demand can also be triggered by a well-phrased question. What is required is a lit-tle more intelligence to filter what we require from ill-posed questions or propositions. If only the medium could respond to: "Describe a dinosaur named Barionix," or "Was Barionix a dinosaur, and if so, what was it like?"

Just imagine the solution to Fermat's last problem, not scribbled on paper and lost forever, but recorded for all time. Or alternatively, imag-ine the many works and ideas of Newton that never saw the light of day. Perhaps more powerfully, we should contemplate artificial intelligence systems able to access such works, the coalescing of myriad concepts and results that currently escape us due to our limited human ability and memory. Perhaps in the future, none of us will die in the strict sense, but our essence, an echo of our passing selves, will live on. Perhaps then we will become hybrid beings, networks of total experi-ence, learning, and understanding continuously incremented by the inputs and interactions of a peripheral work force of individual human minds acting in unison with us. At 52 years old, with another decade or two to realize this world, I may just see you there.

60

Ultimately, literature is nothing but carpentry. With both, you are working with reality, a material just as hard as wood.

Gabriel García Márquez (1985).

TREES, PAPER, AND FRIENDS

Not so long ago people would write on both sides of a sheet of paper, and in some cases horizontally and vertically, to make full use of a very expensive and handmade commodity. Today, it seems we can afford to waste paper, but can we? With millions of book titles in print and billions of copies sitting on shelves worldwide, there has to be a finite limit. After all, this is the planet's forests being transformed into thermal insulation and room decoration at the rate of about 250M tonnes/year. Is this really the right thing to be doing?

No doubt about it, paper is a nice medium, and very convenient. It affords zero bootup time, requires no batteries, and can be conveniently folded into a shirt pocket. Relatively speaking, paper is also very low-cost since we have become very efficient in its manufacture and reprocessing. In this equation we should not dismiss our individual years of dedication to learn to read and write efficiently. The cost of this skill acquisition is unlikely to be overtaken by the average lifetime of paper consumption we could anticipate enjoying. Perhaps surprisingly, the cost of providing a computer screen for life falls into the same cost bracket as the cost of paper we each consume. This means we are becoming extraordinarily efficient, since working on screen gives at least a tenfold gain over paper-based systems.

While in my work I avoid paper like the plague and make every effort to avoid printing anything, I still enjoy the look and feel of the occasional book. For nontechnical works I am happy to buy a paper or hardback and read in my armchair, but textbooks present a major problem. I can never find one book that covers my topic of study; they are always deficient in one regard or another. What I need is the ability to cook my own. A chapter from here, a paragraph from there, and figures and diagrams from another. Come to think about it, I'd like to do this with music CDs and tapes too. They never have my choice or optimum selection and cannot be updated and augmented.

Even with no power of content selection and format cooking, I like music stores that let me sample their products before I buy. The old libraries and bookstores were fun too. I used to enjoy being able to browse, sample, and choose. But now I would like one more degree of freedom: to download and try on my screen, to modify, add to, and compile my own volumes, and then if I really need, to print.

Consider the efficiency of any book you buy. It is hard to exceed 0.02 percent for a novel and 0.2 percent for a textbook. Just think how many times you read your individual books and how many hours they are in your hands during their lifetime. In contrast, and given the ultralow cost of digital storage, the efficiency of information retention and use on a PC (replaced every three years) is likely to exceed 10 percent. In my case I estimate my information storage efficiency to be around 15 percent. I suspect that if you get past 30 percent, you make some dramatic transition into a new class of human.

As I type these words, I am sitting in a forest surrounded by unbounded beauty, trees of all kinds. What are we doing reducing them to pulp just to record our words for a few decades, just to give them the attention of our eyes for an hour or two? I feel kind of comfortable here. . .among friends.

61

*"What lasting joys
the man attend,
who has a polished
female friend."*
Cornelius Whurr (1845)

MY THIRD LOBE

This is the last time I shall sit at this laptop and type anything. Over the past three years this machine has been a faithful companion and has traveled over 500,000 miles, participated in over 1000 presentations, processed over 12,000 e-mail messages, documented innumerable meetings and visits, and recorded all of my writings. But time has run out, and it has become a museum piece, overtaken by technological advance and, sadly, old age. It is worn out by use to the point where all the connectors are sloppy, and even the plastic hand rest is polished by the abrasion of my moving palms. So it really is time to move on.

During our three year partnership, this machine never failed me, always got pictures onto projectors, always got online from any point on the planet. It did everything I demanded and has been the personification of good design and reliability. To me, it has not been just a tool and a third lobe but in a curious way, almost a friend. And now we have to say goodbye.

What to do with this machine? Having pondered this for some time, I have decided to turn it into a time capsule, a message from the past for future generations. As I switch off for the last time, I will leave it looking like the Marie Celeste of the IT world. Completed files, half-finished work, applications, and a few pending mail messages in local folders will all be left as they are at the end of this monologue. It will be a true snapshot of the life of a late 20th century on-line technologist, to be mounted in a perspex display box hung on my office wall.

Later, when the emotional bonds are weaker and I feel we can part company, I plan to consign this friend to a vault to be interred for at least 100 years, sealed for posterity. Imagine now the reaction when it is discovered 100 years from today. No doubt, many of the components will have died, but the technology of that time may be able to power it up and access this electronic vault. How will the technology archaeologist of that time react? "Look, only 0.5 Gbytes of memory on a rotating disc, 20 Mbytes of RAM and a 36 MHz clock, a keyboard and a mouse, a 2D screen of such small size and poor definition, and a combined operating system application pack of less than 80 Mbytes. Wow, how did the owner work? How did he get anything done? How heavy; how did he wear this thing? Oh, I remember, in those days they used to carry them in bags—wonderful. But look at the craftsmanship, hard to beat the old technologies, all hand-assembled you know, not like the machine-built wearables and microimplants today."

In 1997 a new market has been established for antique computers, and I suspect that this laptop will very shortly enter the same category. Old Atari, Apple, and Sinclair machines can now be worth more than their original purchase price to dedicated collectors. Houses, furniture, and cars take 50 or more years to achieve antique status. But because of the accelerating speed of technology development, the time required to achieve this badge is falling exponentially. So on second thought, perhaps I need an active vault that powers up my laptop from time to time and keep it in working order. Perhaps I should also visit my old friend from time to time, just to recall a past electronic life.

62

A WEB OF UNNATURAL LAWS

Our civilization and world of commerce is founded on the processing of atoms—making and shipping things. It is a human-scale world moving at a modest pace, where control and laws are key ingredients to success and sustainability. But we are in the midst of a transformation from a reasonably well-behaved, understood, and comfortable world of randomness to a world of mind-boggling complexity and chaos. Hierarchy and control now have little to offer and constitute a threat to those people and systems that adhere to them.

Many companies, organizations, and managers now see the mean time between surprises as far shorter than the mean time between decisions. The reason? A slow paper-based world of irrelevant processes, backward-looking rules, regulations, and laws being rapidly overtaken by IT. Geography and international boundaries have long been bypassed by radio, TV, and telephone, and are now transcended by computer, optical fiber, and satellite. This is a world dominated by bits, and it is not on a human scale.

There are already mountains of legal and ethical problems presented by the new realms of telemedicine, telecare, tele-education, teleworking, publishing, electronic commerce, and just communicating what and how we wish. Like the control of broadcasting in the past and perhaps the growing drug problem in the future, we may have to abandon all efforts at control on a Web that is naturally out of control.

Soon, a new mechanism in the form of artificial intelligence will introduce a further degree of freedom (or irresponsibility). It is already difficult to detect an electronic crime, define where it was committed, and determine whose laws (if any) were broken and by whom. Even worse, it will be difficult to decide what was responsible. People may not even be involved.

Suppose I sell you an artificial intelligence system that trades on the stock market, manages your bank account, and generally takes you out of the loop of financial management. It makes you progressively richer by trading on the short-term marginals, negotiates the best price with the utilities and food suppliers, and so on. But the program is truly intelligent, and I keep upgrading for you as part of your purchase agreement. Over a period of years it gets much smarter and gets to know you and your needs intimately. In response, you encourage it to be more efficient, take more risks, and generally make more money. Well, it's still not a perfect world, and the IRS remotely logs on to conduct an audit. To our amazement, they discover the system has been committing crimes to make money. Who is responsible, the hardware, software, you, or me?

Clearly, if the law has changed and I have not upgraded your software in accordance with the new legislation, I am culpable. But what if I have gone bankrupt in the intervening period? If you have reloaded an older version of the software because it made more money, or if you have tampered with it, are you obviously guilty, and could it be proved?

If unbeknown to both of us, the software has evolved by mutation and communicated with other systems worldwide to achieve a better performance by circumventing the law, then is it alone guilty? Or are we still culpable, I as the supplier and you as the user, for being irresponsible and not checking up on the system regularly enough?

This may all seem like a radical and remote prospect, but machine-based, peopleless corporations are already in prospect. In such a world, I suspect we will need soft auditors, police, and lawyers.

63

PEOPLE AS BILLBOARDS

Several decades ago an earth-moving plant manufacturer produced hats bearing their company logo. This was emblazoned on the front and used as an advertising gift for good customers. These soon became prized and sought-after items to the extent that demand outstripped supply, and almost by accident, the company discovered that people would pay to get one of their hats. At that time, a more extraordinary move of sector was hard to imagine as they gradually migrated into the clothing market. The now ubiquitous T shirt followed, and sweaters and coats. This was probably the birth of the designer label, and what a counterintuitive outcome. Who could have guessed that people would actually pay to advertise the goods they purchase. Today, people walk about looking like animated billboards, and moreover, they compete to have the latest, most fashionable, and communally acceptable brands of shoes and clothes. Forty years ago this was unimaginable, and impossible.

The rise of the designer label now has the population of the planet vying to pay five to tenfold the market price for every form of visible and invisible clothing, luggage, jewelry, glasses, and more. In a strange inversion of values, people now pay way over the odds to advertise the goods they purchase, and the era of "image is all" now seems to be well established. But it is only recently that the technology to do all this economically has become available. Without computer-controlled knitting, sewing, and embossing machines and a vast range of new materials, we would be constrained to a modest label on the inside, and sober patterns and colors on the outside of everything we wear and carry. And no doubt the world would be a much duller place.

What happens next? What will be the next unexpected, and most likely new trend? What will populations find not only acceptable but so desirable they will be willing to pay for the next communication and advertising privilege? Today, we have a raft of synthetic materials that allow all manner of clothing and wearable items to be fabricated at exceptionally low cost. Anything from plastic sneakers and jewelry to jeans and shirts can be branded with ease. So what might new materials with active programming of color and pattern through heat sensitivity or changing electrostatic charge promote? Or even more radically, there is on the horizon the possibility of electronically programming text, graphics, animation, and, ultimately, shape and size.

Arrive at the office looking like a hippie and switch to pinstripes as you walk through the door. Go to a party and switch to fancy dress on arrival. Connect your shirt or jacket to a PC and load your own pictures, animation, or message. Rent out your chest, back, and legs as advertising space. Integrate these now active surfaces with mobile phone, pager, organizer, and computer and we then become both the medium and the message. Could it be that we will buy fewer clothes with greater programmability and then use them as a primary means of communication.

To date, research into active materials is achieving very modest color and pattern variations at slow rates of change, with only rudimentary modifications to shape possible for semirigid items. But we might anticipate fabricating surfaces with far greater abilities, perhaps approaching today's LCDs. So sometime over the next decade or two, we are likely to see fabrics becoming an active part of the IT infrastructure. Once active, it will be hard to resist programmable clothing and the new means of advertising and narrowcasting they will bring.

64

"Work is life . . .
and without it,
there's nothing but fear
and insecurity."
John Lennon (1969)

ANOTHER HOTEL ROOM

Well, here I am at the end of a long day having traveled halfway round the planet. It is 01.45 hours UK time. I have been on the move for 15 hours and awake for over 18. I struggle through the door into another hotel room that certainly qualifies as anytime, anywhere. I'm tired and the bed looks inviting, but it is time to unpack, iron another shirt, have a shower, and get on-line.

Having completed all my domestic tasks, I turn to my laptop, with her batteries recharging. She shows no sign of tiredness or the ravages of international travel. Getting on-line is an almost painless process, provided there is a socket on the phone in the room or a mobile phone connection. At this hour my most frustrating moments come about through the proliferation of new carrier start-ups and service providers with their expanding catalogue of operating quirks. And of course, there are also the hotel chains, who see it as reasonable to grossly overcharge for calls or block telephone charge card usage. This is all compounded by the unseen compression of signals and diversity of routing negotiated in real time to get the lowest bit cost. Such practices are very restrictive and complex and at worst can be hugely expensive, with a tenfold or more markup on the normal price of a call. There can also be huge variations in circuit and connection quality, and to my mind such practices should be outlawed. But by and large, a little engineering cunning overcomes such obstacles, and it is rare for me to fail to get on-line at a good price and with good quality transmission within 20 minutes or so.

In this hotel room my witching hour has long gone, and having logged on, I start work. There seems to be no way of knowing or guessing how much work there will be in the stack and how long it will take to complete. But my mind is on sleep and the bed beckons.

If only I could be on-line all the time, I could perhaps avoid the peaks of demand over which I have no control, or could I? How come there was nothing outstanding at 21.00 hours as I boarded an intermediate flight, and now there is a flood? On close examination of working practices, we seem to have increasing numbers of people scheduling e-mail sessions. Time is actually set aside to sit in front of the screen to attack large blocks of mail. People being the way they are, and the corporate environment being the way it is, we seem to have large numbers selecting almost the same period to attack their accumulated mail. As a direct result, synchronized mail now starts to arrive in tidal waves by time zone. This generates electronic and human congestion that is not good news for networks or the individual.

Regimentation in an electronic environment is not a good practice. Could it be that that the nine-to-five paper mindset is now moving onto the net in large numbers as corporations move into "e-working?" Well, it certainly feels that way, and if so, they need to be encouraged to change their working practices to become far more opportunistic. Observing mail arriving in my office resembles waiting for a bus or taxi. It always seem to come in bunches.

Having cleared the desk after this long day, I slide between the sheets hoping that the leap across time zones does not see my next breakfast accompanied by another tidal wave of mail from unseen, but synchronized hosts.

65

VIRTUAL CHILDREN

Children occupy a special place in the world of primates and many other strains of carbon evolution. For our species they represent an unsurpassed investment and sacrifice of self interest. There is no business case or training course for successful parenting. We go forward generation after generation, trusting to luck that we will realize a satisfactory outcome—a reasonable and responsible member of society. In reality the spread of outcomes is very wide and mostly acceptable. But there cannot be a parent alive who has not seen some feature of their offspring's behavior that they have not fully liked, agreed with, or objected too. A most sobering experience is to see your own faults and failings reflected in your own child. At best, parents can take corrective action, but the final mature outcome is still uncertain and attempts at correction may even be counterproductive. And there is no alternative, we have to watch the emergent behavior of each child and successive generations as they learn and adapt to their changing environments.

So far, carbon life systems have evolved a range of sensors, emotions, communication strategies, and rule sets that ensure the survival of individual species. On the average, love and kindness overpower hate and meanness; care overpowers neglect; collaboration is better than isolation; and we choose to take sensible risks, fight for survival, and be benevolent. Our natural tendency is not to kill but to nurture life. A large proportion of this appears to be fundamental to our nature.

We are just born that way, and if we were not, there would be little hope of surviving very long. The downside of all this is that it places constraints on the way and speed we can evolve. This process of change and adaptation turns out to be very slow and measured, which is not always a desirable feature.

In silicon systems we are still writing the initial rules, discovering the opportunities, and adapting the technology, because we have newfound degrees of freedom. Why ape the limited world of carbon life when there are new opportunities? When we consider software or robotic reproduction in the context of children, there are no moral constraints on the number of sexes involved, monogamy, the mechanisms of birth, or indeed, the quotient of success. In fact, all of these carbon constraints and human values are an impediment to rapid evolution. A "child" may now be born of parents in a system that coldly judges the performance of this new entity. If it does not measure up to requirements, does not represent a sufficient advance, it can be terminated. The observed attributes it had, good and bad, can be fed back into the parents to modify or steer the genetic features of the next "child." So between mature generations, a raft of "virtual children" can be tried and tested, sequentially refined, and used to create the best or nearest fit to requirements. This sees each generation of new parents capable of making giant evolutionary leaps in ability. They also show a better ability to adapt to a fast-changing environment.

In telecommunications and computer networks today, we are witnessing a rapid evolution of peripheral equipments and services. These include millions of fax machines, pagers, mobile phones, and on-line PCs in less than a decade, and there is much more to come. Conventional software production techniques for superreliable and adaptive networks and service provision is looking increasingly difficult, and by 2005 it might be impossible. But it might just be that terminating software children for not living up to our expectations could prove to be the answer.

66

"Change begets change.
Nothing propagates so fast."
Charles Dickens (1844)

SOFT STRESS

Among the most stressful things we do, being born, starting school, leaving home, driving fast, changing jobs, buying a house, getting married, having children, getting divorced, and dying are probably at the top of the list. Recently, there have been additions to this critical list that include changing computer hardware, operating system, and applications. The stress level is often increased with a coincidental job or project change. When you really need to work fast and the project or job is new, the last thing you need is an arm wrestling contest with some new and perverse IT system.

If you work in a fast-moving industry or have a pressured job, IT is an essential tool, and years of experience may find you confident at mastering technological challenge. But get a software upgrade and the stress soon builds. In the last few years I have watched generations of word processors, spreadsheets, and graphics packs transcend the useful and user-friendly to become fiendishly complex. From auto-spelling checks that irritatingly pop onto the screen as you type to the graphics by questionnaire that realizes the wrong format in five easy stages, some of the changes beggar belief. Not only do they consume a vast amount of storage, they reconfigure commands, change names and locations, and present a vast range of never-to-be-used (or discovered) options that just confuse users.

Recently, I embarked upon a self-inflicted experiment, simultaneously changing my platform, operating system, and upgrading all applications. My advice to anyone contemplating anything remotely similar is don't. What a nightmare. My work pressure continued, but I could not complete anything fast enough to overcome this triple adversity. Everything was different— keyboard, mouse, screen, functions— everything. All visual, tactile, and audio clues were changed. I was a stranger in a strange land. My output dropped to <10 percent of normal, and within an hour I reverted to my old system to catch up and restore some semblance of normality.

My ultimate solution was to move platform and operating system and use my old application set. Then I embarked on a gradual step-by-step upgrade of applications. Why bother? Well, I feel duty bound to live at the edge and try all the latest bells and whistles, but from an efficiency and effectiveness point of view, I have to admit that I have not become one iota more productive. The only advantage I have realized is that of being compatible and up to date. And I must confess to a growing feeling of resentment at continuously having to upgrade for nothing. I want speed and effectiveness, applications customized to me personally, and not a mountain of stuff designed for all humanity.

Among the software perversity I also discovered a brand new feature— biodegradability. An application that started off fast and effective, got slower and slower until it became unusable. This I just did not have the patience to sort, and it was deleted.

It can only be that commercial considerations preclude us having a cut down and basic set of applications that are backward, forward, and sideways compatible. Writing a letter, book, business case, or report does not demand the capabilities of an entire publishing industry. Nor does a presentation pack need the capabilities of Hollywood, or for that matter, a spreadsheet the ability to predict the weather. Why not a basic subset that we can upgrade with modules we individually need. Alternatively, how about intelligent applications that customize the whole to our personal needs and the way we work. Roll on the day— and a less stressful IT existence.

67

"For a few golden sentences
we will turn over and actually read
a volume of four or five hundred pages."

Ralph Waldo Emerson (1841)

WASTED BITS AND HANDBOOKS

Having been an engineer in the IT industry for more than 30 years, I religiously refuse to read handbooks. Almost without exception, I plunge straight into a new technology and set off on a voyage of discovery, gradually unraveling how it operates. I take the view that if I cannot do this successfully, it is the fault of the designer and not mine. For as long as I can remember, I have also refused to read books on software programming or attend courses on the subject. So far, I have become reasonably proficient with desktop applications and have attained some skill with the common languages by unpicking the constructs of others. My other routes to success include watching and talking to experienced practitioners and, I must confess, the occasional sneaky look in the book when really desperate.

Software manuals are not good bedtime reading, and they always seem to be as perverse as the products they describe. On most occasions I fail to find what I am searching for and resort to consulting an expert. Another useful mechanism is the serendipitous flash of realization. Recently, these seem to have been arriving thick and fast in sympathy with a spate of application upgrades by everyone around me. Here are a couple of examples from my word processing package.

When I first started writing my newspaper column, each 600 word item required a reasonably standard 16 kBytes of hard disc. After about three months I received a software upgrade and suddenly the storage demand for my 600 words increased to 24 kBytes or more. With the latest upgrade, I have seen an increased demand for at least 46 kBytes, and the article that prompted me to unpick the software had grown to 150 kBytes.

Now, 150 kBytes for 600 words is 250 bits/word. Assuming that my words are, on average, five characters plus a space, which makes 6, at 8 bits/character, I should only need 48 bits/word. Somewhere, there appears to be an excessive overhead of around 200 bits/word. Line spacing, return, punctuation, case, and other formatting information might increase the total by another 10 percent or so, but this hardly impacts the unaccounted waste.

This prompted me to start playing, and I soon discovered that every modification is recorded but hidden from view. So a virgin draft document will accumulate all the modifications of later editing. Looking over my texts, I discovered that the easy documents to produce were compact, while anything with multiple contributors and edits could be four or five times bigger than logic would predict.

A simple solution to all this came to mind. I saved the 150k monster as an earlier version of my package and it reverted to only 8k. What a saving. Incidentally, 8k is the smallest file size on my machine and is dictated by the memory allocation structure.

My next thought went to the documents other people had sent me. I selected a sample of overweight candidates and set about probing the contents. Sure enough, in every case I was able to see the original draft and all subsequent modifications. Apparently, the authors were unaware that this was happening and did not secure their unintended communication.

Another interesting feature of this investigation was the existence of a class of virus that embeds itself in the macros of the package. This can be overcome by disabling the macros if not required. Alternatively, saving down a couple of application versions also does a good job.

Further investigation revealed similar problems in my spreadsheet and presentation pack. But nowhere in the documentation could I find adequate explanations or warnings. The final score: engineering instinct 1, handbooks 0.

68

*"We should take care
not to make the intellect our god;
it has, of course, powerful muscles,
but no personality."*

Albert Einstein (1950)

MAN MAGNIFIERS

When Sigourney Weaver faced the horrific creature in the final act of Alien 2, we all cheered as she slid into the exoskeleton "man magnifier" and prepared to do battle. Here was a lone woman pitched against a creature of far superior strength, agility, and killing power. But the nth generation backhoe digger enhanced Sigourney's strength and abilities over tenfold, and she was more than a match for this out-of-water shark. Here the ingenuity of the human overcame a formidable foe by the amplification of basic muscular capabilities through technology. How strange, then, that as Deeper Blue took out Gary Kasporov you could hear the gasp of horror. Machine beats the Chess Grand Master; Kasporov, sidelined by the silicon beast. Conversely, we would not think of entering a weight lifting competition against a crane. It would just be accepted as a nonmatch. Why is it that physical leverage is okay, but the intellectual equivalent is not?

Most of us flip a light switch, control an elevator, use a pocket calculator, drive a car, cook a pizza, or make a phone call without giving a thought to the technology controlling the process. Who cares? Yet the prospect of machines smarter than people instantly worries most of us. Why? No one would try arm wrestling an assembly-line robot, or for that matter, try to compute and manipulate graphics faster than a PC. But then again, we no longer perceive these as a threat. They are not seen to be smart, intelligent, or potential rivals. But don't they do their job with more accuracy and efficiency than the humans they displaced?

Probably a science fiction industry that continually depicts technology as predominantly malevolent has a lot to do with the public perception. Curiously, Commander Data and the Shape Shifters of Star Trek do not fill us with horror despite their obvious superiority. On the other hand, Terminator can make your skin crawl. So is it merely a matter of form, some threshold of appearance and action that signals a level of humanity that makes an entity acceptable to us? Even HAL in 2001 seemed menacing through voice and words alone. So do we merely have to find some anthropomorphic threshold to give our technology that necessary human, animal, or toylike touch? I suspect so. In Japan the population ascribes automobiles a happy, sad, or angry demeanor from the appearance of the radiator grill, so why not computers too?

Computers are already the most effective and powerful mind magnifiers we ever produced, and they look set to continue to encroach further. Their past claim to fame was control, memory, and raw number crunching. Today, this has expanded to analysis, modeling, visualization, and decision support. They are now set to enter our previously exclusive territory of logic, reason, and rationale. As with previous encroachments, they will help us discover new ways of solving problems and understanding phenomena, and thereby enhance our limited species. Remember, without computers we would not understand the details of chaos, weather systems, epidemiology, DNA, the turbulent flow of air over an aircraft wing, our own genome, and very much more. Relatively speaking, we would know nothing if it were not for computers. Human minds were, and still are, inadequate for the job of tackling problems of modest, let alone, immense complexity.

Perhaps to make all this acceptable, the quality we will have to build into future machines will be magnanimity and tolerance to our inadequacies and foibles. Apparently, it is okay to compute numbers faster than we do, but not to reason.

69

"I confidently predict the collapse of capitalism. . . . Something will go wrong . . . the banking system will collapse . . . and we will be left having to barter to stay alive."

Margaret Drabble (1993)

BITS FOR BARTER

While our economy is definitely embedded in a capitalist system, it has its roots firmly fixed in a past of barter. The impracticality of barter on a large scale prompted the world of coins, paper, checks and plastic that is now dominant. This in turn may be eclipsed by electronic cash, which will offer even more flexibility and convenience. Ultimately, micropayments could rapidly revolutionize the whole concept of money, though it is a recently voiced concept that has only been engineered at the prototype level. But there is also a new option that is prompting hidden trade that could build fast—bits for barter. Electronic working makes it easy to advertise atoms and bits for sale and find a match in the global marketplace.

Living in a village, town, or city gives the opportunity for a black market economy of people trading goods, skills, services, and assistance on the nod. However, it is an economy that will always be limited by the bounds of word of mouth advertising and communication. So it tends to be an activity between friends and acquaintances, people who are known to and trust each other. In this context we should recognize that banks and financial institutions are primarily in the trust business. Their role overtook and replaced large-scale barter because they provided a mediating mechanism. Money replaced pigs, goats, corn, sweat, and toil. Along with this trust transition to money came the standardization of price and the efficiency of the "haggle-free" market.

The wheel turns full circle, and centuries after the invention of money and the rise of financial houses, a new world has emerged, and the possibility of a global barter economy. How much easier it is to advertise and trade on the net—no frontiers, no barriers, no limits. All bits are potentially for sale, for more and different bits. Even atoms and services can be traded. Inspect, try and test the goods on the net, agree on a trade, and send by snailmail. Need some advice or a service? Access it all on-line and pay by bits or goods. Somewhere on the planet, someone has what you want and needs what you want to be rid of. Only the advertising and mediation process stops this from coming about, but the agents to do it are coming. Soon we will be able to send out the:"I need this game and have these games to trade" agent. Or will it be: "I have these skills and will do x hours of work for this software or hardware."

The global black market economy is reckoned in $100s of billions. Here, then, is a mechanism for it to get even bigger. Can it be we will see electronic trading posts—frontier style—with human agents haggling in bytes? Or will we be more relaxed in the bit world and be driven by perceived quality and need rather than raw quantity and availability. Duplication, pirating, modification, and additions to soft products will then have a whole new meaning.

How do you collect taxes to support the infrastructure of a nation when no money is exchanged, or is in such small increments you cannot afford to collect it or even police the system? With micropayments, a million transactions of a penny is bad enough, but charging tax at 17 percent of each exchange is impossible. Having no means of interception and recording for this exchange of bits goods and services is even worse. This could become a macroeconomy of micro things, well beyond any fiscal process yet in place or conceived.

70

NO ABSOLUTES

One of the key differences between folklore, superstition, and science is the lack of absolutes. Science is dynamic and dominated by uncertainty. The latest state of understanding is dictated by models and theory linked by experimentation and observation to the world in which we live. In contrast, the alternatives offer the comfort of certainty, with rules and beliefs that endure for centuries and remain unaltered even in the face of irrefutable evidence and knowledge. A flat earth at the center of a solar system and universe were established wisdoms that took thousands of years to overturn. And no doubt, there are more discoveries and surprises to come as we progressively examine and question our own construction, existence, and purpose. When we have sufficient knowledge to challenge the divinity of life, we will face some mighty conceptual barriers.

In the absence of any real evidence, individuals and society have a tendency to react adversely to the new as if under threat. Witness Dolly and cloning. Cloning is not photocopying, and it poses no threat, but you might have thought from the media hysteria it was the beginning of the end. Currently, mobile phones and other communication devices are a hot topic, as their radio emissions may pose a new threat in the form of cancer stimulation. Of course, we should react with caution and be responsible, but as yet there is no positive evidence, only fear. In fact, the evidence is currently in favor of mobile phones being safe and an insignificant risk. For sure, we should continue monitoring the situation, but there are far greater risks when driving a car or crossing the road. Perhaps we should also look at how many people bask in the sun for hours or have their microwave ovens conveniently mounted at head height. Does anyone bother to check for safe sun exposure times or radiation leaks from their ovens caused by abuse and poor maintenance? Given the hundreds of watts ovens generate, we perhaps ought to treat them with a little more caution and respect.

Consider now the ludicrous situation with the internationally agreed safety levels for nuclear radiation. Here, the safe levels are defined to be below that which most of us naturally receive by just sitting at home in our armchairs. Certainly anyone living in a rocky area will be receiving a natural background radiation dose that well exceeds that defined as safe. Interestingly, no one worries about the carbon 14 emitted from the exhaust stacks of coal-fired power stations, which cumulatively exceeds the radiation leak at Three Mile Island.

Japan is the only country with a population that has been exposed to an atomic bomb, and the horror of these events probably did much to foster the "all radiation is bad" thinking that prevails globally today. But recent evidence seems to indicate that those exposed to the lower levels of nuclear radiation during the two bombing events are, on average, actually living longer than those far removed and totally insulated. Could it be that this is the first evidence that low-level radiation is actually good for us? This is an area that we should really start to study and understand rather than get upset because it might overturn our dogma and accumulated fears.

Just suppose for a moment that we need radiation as a primary agent in the evolutionary process. What if it is the vital noise function, the randomness agent, that necessary to promote mutation in cells and gene strings? It might just be that it is the prime mover, the core of life itself—in moderation of course.

71

*Who shall set a limit
to the influence of
a human being?*

Ralph Waldo Emerson (1860)

NO MORE OUTPUT

For me, living on the technological edge for over a decade has become both an operational necessity and a way of life. As far as I can estimate, my work output has increased tenfold during the last decade through the judicious use of the latest technology, management, and working practices. But I have hit the wall; I just cannot do, achieve, or output more. By my reckoning, I am getting the most out of the combination of me and IT. At home, office, and on the move, I always have access to a machine and I'm seldom off-line. This being the case, I ask the obvious question: What next? How do we continue to ride the wave of exponential change and increased productivity that all generations have sustained since Adam?

Well, there are marginal gains to be had by fine-tuning my technology and time management but nothing significant. I have explored my abilities to the edge of physical and mental exhaustion, and the onset of nausea from information overload. My recent computer hardware upgrade and simultaneous software downgrade have resulted in huge performance improvements. More or less all delays between hand, screen, and eye have been removed. Applications open instantaneously once booted up and files save in a second. My network connection has been upgraded too, so e-mail, Web, and other connections are also very fast.

I now need something more fundamental to augment my limited biology. A truly intelligent technology is the only hope I can see of being more productive. Of course, fundamentally changing the nature of companies and civilization is another possibility to explore. No doubt this will happen, but in the wake of IT, and then more slowly. Historically, it always has, and we have never been prepared in advance. So here is my wish list for the next lurch forward.

Beyond machines we can converse with and wear, plus an ability to autonomously communicate with everything, I rate increased intelligence most highly. Instead of searching for data and graphics, I need systems that search out, select, refine, and then push me. I would also welcome a degree of anticipation in this process, plus some serendipity, interaction, and learning. The "Daily Me" would be a real boon—personalized news and information tailored to my needs and interests.

On the people front, I would value recognition systems that automatically capture the image, name, organization, and meeting details of everyone I interact with. If I could later relate and recall by vague descriptors and association, along the lines: balding professor of computer science from the U.S. I met at a conference four years ago in Paris, my system should then be smart enough to bring that person to the fore, including all the relevant information. This would counteract my increasing forgetfulness, which I fear accelerates with age.

Beyond this, I would endow machines with the ability to instantly analyze data and situations automatically, or upon a simple verbal request. Even better still, I would have them bringing to bear past history and experience of machines and people as part of the process. At this stage an artificial imagination is perhaps asking too much, but a generic modeling ability to help cope with the complexity of business, technology, and life in general would enhance me significantly.

Any travel substitute and communication technology that enhanced all human communication would, I suspect, see the biggest saving of all. But beyond all this, it would appear that the fundamental limit is us, our biology and sociology. So our society probably stands to see even more radical and significant change.

72

"For time is the
longest distance
between two places."
Tennessee Williams (1914-83)

REFLECTIONS ON BALLOONS

Given the demand for mobile communication, radio spectrum, and orbital slots for satellites, not to mention the launch and maintenance costs, it seems extraordinary that no one is exploiting modern balloon technology. At an altitude of 10 km, a balloon has a line of sight surface horizon of some 350 km, and therefore a radio communication footprint of the order 700 km diameter.

Just consider the downside of satellites. The geostationary orbit alone now harbors thousands of new, unused, and expired satellites that constitute an expensive band of clutter. It is also a growing junkyard in space that conveys a small fraction of the bits transported on terrestrial and undersea optical fiber cables. Geostationary satellite channels suffer a transmission delay dictated by distance in excess of 0.3 s. This delay, combined with a modest amount of echo, can make it difficult to hold a telephone conversation. Of course, for broadcast applications delay is not an issue. In contrast, a North Atlantic optical fiber cable only introduces about 0.03 s, which is indistinguishable to human ear and eye. Geostationary satellites also require large antennas and high transmitter powers, and sensitive receivers are to overcome the path loss and adverse weather conditions.

Soon we will also have hundreds of low-cost low earth orbit (LEO) nonsynchronous satellites in orbits between 1000 km and 3000 km. Being low altitude, they will allow the use of smaller antennas, lower power, and cruder receivers for handheld mobile and portable applications. Of course, being in LEO, the much shorter transmission distances will see delays more or less comparable to cables. But then again, they are not locked into a sustainable orbit and will fall out of the sky far more often than the geostationary counterparts. So a network of such satellites will require a continuous launch program for replacements.

A net result of all this should be more mobile communication capacity at the expense of an increasingly cluttered sky. Ultimately, the multilayered orbits could constitute a threat and limitation to future space exploration—an orbital minefield in the making. But balloon technology offers an alternative and far cheaper solution.

Modern balloons are safe, reliable, inexpensive, and capable of lifting substantial payloads to significant heights. A network of only four to six balloons hovering at 10 km could service the whole of the UK to the extent that they could illuminate the Welsh and Scottish mountains to provide a universal service currently inaccessible to equatorial satellites. At lower altitudes more would be required, of course, and perhaps 10 might be acceptable. Telephone, data, radio, and TV access would be possible at low cost using microwave radio, possibly augmented by infrared optical beams. For some applications a metalized balloon might suffice as a passive reflector; a mirror in the sky.

A further advantage beyond the very low payload and launch costs is the ease of platform access for equipment repairs and upgrades. So what is the downside? There are only two: the tethering and/or positioning technology and the threat to air traffic. A cable anchor to the ground is the most attractive tethering solution as it can serve as an anchor and a signaling and control medium. For obvious reasons, this would need to be clearly marked visually and for radar. It would also need to be protected by a no-flying zone in the same manner that TV and radio masts are to date.

There is, however, a further alternative: tetherless positioning above the air lanes with robotic thrustors to hold a fixed position relative to the planet's surface. While this would necessitate a power plant, fuel, refueling, and hot standby craft, it is not out of the question. It only needs engineering.

73

*"How few things can a man measure
with the tape of his understanding?
How many greater things might
he be seeing in the meanwhile!"*

Henry David Thoreau (1851)

NOTIONS AND GUESSES

When I was a student, I had the benefit of some outstanding teachers. Many of them were seasoned engineers and physicists from industry who taught me much more than principles and theory; they imparted intuition and insight. Among the many guiding principles I gained from this seminal period were these important and vital words: "In mathematics and science it is acceptable to have no answer. However, in engineering this is never admissible. You must always get an answer, even if it is the wrong one. Engineers have to start somewhere, and no answer means you cannot even start. If you can get started, you will rapidly iterate toward an acceptable solution. So always get an answer."

Another of my teachers was a physicist turned mathematician who labored with me as I struggled with the concepts of partial differential equations and variational calculus. Over one difficult and protracted problem, he suddenly looked me in the eye and said: "When tackling any problem, it is always worth stopping to think what the answer might be."

In both cases these were timely and prophetic words, and today they are even moreso. We are now squaring up to a highly complex and nonlinear world, and we face a future largely dominated by problems we cannot solve by any linear, well-behaved, or even known means. So it is essential that we develop new insight through direct experience. That "straw man" solution and well-founded guess are becoming more vital by the day. Finding solutions for the future means starting somewhere. So what might we guess for the most important and necessary conditions for life and intelligence?

Currently, there are no satisfactory definitions for life or artificial life, intelligence or artificial intelligence. At this juncture we just do not have the experience and basic information to coin adequate descriptors. Indeed, it may prove impossible to produce complete and all-embracing definitions. This is not only because we do not understand these domains with sufficient precision but perhaps more significantly because evolution never stops, and our understanding may never catch up or keep pace. Furthermore, we have a very limited view of what life and intelligence is. We tend to be restricted to a carbon-based view. So here are two partial listings of what may be the essential defining properties that may ultimately turn out to be neither inclusive or exclusive.

For life: a birth- death/creation-destruction process; mutation; evolution; chaos; competition; communication; collaboration; cooperation; energy conservation; entropy; growth; a changing environment.

For intelligence: memory; decision-making; information subsumption; communication; cognition; contemplation—waiting to react; uncertainty; a degree of autonomy, predictability, and unpredictability; more input than output data.

We have only recently discovered that self-organization and chaos are vital ingredients for carbon-based life, with all known living things existing on the edge of strange attractors. The same may turn out to be true of data and information. Perhaps data becomes information on the edge. Life and intelligence seem to demand (or create) a risky, nonlinear, and uncertain world. For humankind this is a new and largely unexplored paradigm that we are becoming a part of, rather than just subject to, and have yet to fully understand. But it is obviously a very rich field, given the estimated 30 to 70 million nonhuman species currently sharing planet earth with us.

Today, we have a responsibility for the stewardship of a planet. Curiously, we are not mere caretakers, but a part of the ecosystem itself. Soon, we may find ourselves responsible for a new dimension to this system as we extend into a new world of silicon—my guess.

74

*"If Aristotle were alive today,
he'd have a talk show."*
Timothy Leary (1989)

SUPER SIDEWALKS

Physical transport has evolved footpaths, sidewalks, streets, roads, highways, rivers, canals, railway and tram lines, shipping lanes, and layers of flight paths. This variety is necessary to cope with a vast range of goods and people movement spanning the pedestrian, horse and cart, train, car, jumbo jet, and ocean liner. To replace this variety with a single unified system of physical transport is clearly impossible and undesirable. Even matter transportation would be unlikely to serve all our needs efficiently.

In telecommunications we currently use copper and fiber cables, free-space optics, and terrestrial and satellite radio as the traffic lanes for bits. The way we organize information on these bearers relies on a limited range of opportunity. Time, space, frequency, wavelength, and code are the principal degrees of freedom. But it is worth noting that frequency, wavelength, and coding are not fundamental, they are no more than abstractions of space and time. However, the limitations of physics and engineering present them as powerful opportunities for the packing and selection of signals.

In broadcast systems we use frequency, or wavelength (they are the same thing expressed in two different ways) slots to carry and identify individual radio and TV stations. When digital broadcast takes off, we will also include time and, later, coding as additional channel and information selection mechanisms. In broadcast no attempt is made to use space as a selector. Information is sprayed everywhere. Everyone can see it. The same is generally true of satellite and mobile telephones, where the use of space as a selection mechanism is minimal. Such systems lack any real focus beyond the size of the radio footprint or cell defined by antenna systems and transmitter power. In contrast, free-space optical systems and microwave radio links employ spatial focusing to constrain signal energy to defined physical locations. Alternatively, copper and optical fiber cables route information with great precision straight to the office and home, telephone, television, computer, or whatever.

So when we examine telecommunication and computer networks, we find a very interesting range of selection processes. In telephone systems time and space are dominant, and this is also the case for computer LANs. Cable TV, on the other hand, is dominantly analogue and employs frequency and space. To date, few if any network systems employ all the degrees of freedom—time, frequency/wavelength, space, and coding—for effective communication. Most use two, and few systems use three.

Another important network feature is the information flow symmetry, or lack of it. This spans broadcast and CATV, which are totally asymmetric—studio to listener and viewer, and LANs, which are often partially asymmetric, depending on the user group, to the telephone, which tends to be wholly symmetric. What a soup of interesting combinations our IT world has become.

From all the media hype and political hyperbole we might be excused for thinking that someone somewhere had a grand plan, a design, for the information "superhighway." Unfortunately, this is not the case. No one knows how to combine all the options to simultaneously deliver broadcast radio and TV, Internet, telephony, and more in a unified way. It would seem clear that we have to combine all the modes—time, frequency/wavelength, space, and perhaps coding. Crudely, what a lesser choice gives us is: the telephone network—a footpath; cable and broadcast—a one-way street; LANs—a road under constant repair, cellular radio—a country lane. Unless we simultaneously access time, space and frequency/wavelength, we stand as much chance of realizing a superhighway as getting the USS Enterprise cruising on US101, and the delays will be similar.

75

WASTED LIFE

Every Sunday morning I wade through the pages of my newspaper desperately looking for something to read. If I chance on an article of likely interest, it is quickly scanned and I either decide to read or move on. Should I decide to read, then the article is ripped out by the page and put on a select stack. After about an hour, my scanning and reading is complete and the whole is dispatched to the bin. Of late, I have been unable to find much worth reading. Some weekends I don't find anything at all. What a waste of time. One hour each Sunday spent looking for something to read is just over two days a year.

Suppose I have another 25 years to live. I will have wasted over 50 days of it scanning Sunday newspapers. But even worse, my nonweekend efforts add a further 20 minutes or so each day expended in the same search-and-read routine. This wastes two more hours per week and adds another four days a year, bringing my 25 year expectancy total to 100 days. This sobering realization prompted me to look at magazines, technical journals. At a modest estimate, these account for about as much again, about six days a year. So, about a year of my assumed remaining 25 year total could be wasted just looking for things to read. Of this total, I suspect that less than 10 percent will be worthwhile in the long run.

As I have a vested interest in my future, I decided to study the time wasted in my life over a four-month period. Here are my average figures to date in hours per week: Waiting in line—1.72. Dealing with junk mail—0.23. Sitting in traffic jams—2.34. Waiting for food—3.16. Unwanted e-mail—0.22. Waiting for people who are late—0.15. Waiting for rail, bus, and air transport—2.61. This lot totals 10.43 hours per week. Nearly half a day a week is lost, and those responsible are stealing my life. This is around 25 days a year and 625 days out of my assumed 25 remaining years, a loss of over 1.7 years.

Given the crudity of my measurements and the limited measures I have chosen, I nevertheless stand to lose at least 3 of my 25 years in wasted time. I suspect I could find an additional one-year loss if I counted the time trying to contact people, fix software and systems, and the like. But even a four year loss is overshadowed by the time wasted sleeping, bodily ablutions, and such, which in my case currently amounts to some 10 years.

So an estimated 56 percent of my future will go up in smoke through the inefficiencies of human biology and society. For the moment we can do little about our biological needs, but we can reduce the other losses. The hardware, software, networks, and logistical systems necessary to improve our effectiveness are available. They only require developing and deploying to eradicate waiting in line, traffic delays, and the archaic scanning of paper for news. Video conferencing, telepresence, and electronic working and commerce will all help. The opportunity is huge. Those at the forefront of technology are achieving 10 times more per year than a decade ago. So recovering 4 years in the next 25 would be equivalent to more than a human working lifetime 10 years ago. And technology realizes a compound interest result that magnifies our abilities year on year. So the overall potential is far greater, but somehow I still feel cheated.

76

*"I speak Spanish to God,
Italian to women, French to men
and German to my horse."*

Charles V, King of Spain (1500-1558)

DIGITAL DO-LITTLE

Like the development of human equivalents, computer languages are also dynamic, with a history of success, failure, birth, and death on an increasingly complex scale. Just as Latin is a dead language but still provides some roots for modern development, a succession of machine-based languages provides a platform for increasing sophistication and ease of use. The binary instruction sets used in the early machines have long been surpassed by higher levels of abstraction. In turn, this has allowed more people direct access to machine-based computation. As a result, many children today would be afforded genius status by the computer programmer standards of 30 years ago.

On this digital journey there have been many surprises, with the against-the-odds survival of the not-so-fit for purpose over what at the time were considered the very best engineered solutions. The reason? Well, they were good enough, and they achieved critical mass of adoption. COBOL, for example, is still the dominant computer programming language. This relic of the 1960s lives on in many business systems and appears set to survive quite a while yet. There are even large quantities of ALGOL, FORTRAN, and BASIC still in use.

While modern systems employ C and its variants, HTML, Visual BASIC, and an expanding variety of graphics-based languages, it is interesting to unpick the code to discover the remnants of earlier products that hark back to the machine code of the fifties and sixties. This is perhaps not surprising, given our experience with Latin, but what is amazing is the dramatic change in hardware and operating systems.

By and large, human language developed alongside the encephalization of our wetware. Human brain-size growth is currently seen to have been co-driven by the development of our sensory system and hunting skills. The need to throw projectiles accurately seems to have been a key, if not the primary contributor. But, no doubt, our need to communicate in groups was also an important factor and an integral part of that encephalization process.

While evolutionary pressure to compete and survive demanded better sensory, manipulation, and communication skills, language development faltered and became static for many tribes and nations. It would appear that our rise to *numero uno* was coincident with our brains reaching a maximum practical size. So we became static machines as evolutionary pressures receded and encephalization ceased. Perhaps not surprisingly, then, all major language development beyond this point seems to have been engendered by technological developments. Machines provided both the pressure for and the means to develop human language and communication further.

Unlike the biological world, silicon systems continue to experience the simultaneous evolution and growth of both hardware and software. But even more impressive are the multiple and increasingly sophisticated operating systems and languages being developed at the same time. In carbon terms this is analogous to a new species evolving every few generations to continue the same line of language development, and this with no significant sensory input other than that provided by us, and no conscious understanding of evolutionary pressure to evolve faster. We have become the source of those inputs for the machines. We are both the senses and the competitive element.

Nowhere in the carbon world can I find a direct analogy to this line of development. It far outweighs the common genetic heritage of our species that links us to all other vertebrates. As machines develop further, our integration into their development cycle will become more critical. Hopefully we will see a greater symbiosis of humans with machines.

Not many people try to talk to the animals, but it is increasingly essential that they do so with the machines.

77

"Nations!
What are nations? . . .
It is individuals that
populate the world."
Henry David Thoreau (1906)

HYPERGEOGRAPHY

Our understanding of the way our society and resources are distributed and operate has been shaped by a very practical but limited visualization of time and space. Most can appreciate and understand three spatial dimensions, the passage of time, direction, velocity, location, past, present, future, and epoch. Generally speaking, our five senses have been adequate to cope and deal with the world we consider natural. We have become the masters of this geography; space has been conquered and we can travel almost anywhere. Time, however, remains the biggest challenge. It is ill understood and increasingly in short supply, and is perhaps our most valuable commodity.

When we move to the world of the bit, we encounter a new geography of multiple dimensions. This world is a networked n-dimensional space of multiple copies, existence, connectivity, locations, and forms. Our concepts of a physical geography do not easily translate into this new hypergeographic world. Information can be simultaneously distributed or clustered, singular or plural, static or dynamic, living or dead, past or present, real-time, warped, accelerated, or delayed. Most of these states appear unnatural and exceptional to us, given our limited physical experience and history.

Sitting in front of the screen, we afford ourselves the illusion of two- or three-dimensional pictures of the complex bit world. This is becoming a primary limitation, with our best efforts posing virtual world representations of electronic libraries, bookshelves, offices, and stores, depicted in the familiar framework of home, office, and town. Personally, I find some of this more than irritating. In the real world I am accustomed to the fact that my body has to transport my brain from my desk to the bookshelf or from the meat counter to checkout. But when designers put me in a virtual library or store, this limitation is still imposed. Why? In the bit world there are no physical limitations, and if I can see what I want, then I don't want to wait. I want it instantly by click or voice command. The artificial illusion of a physical space and time delay offer us nothing in this world, apart from a frame of reference for navigation. The realization of instant access seems the more important but neglected parameter.

Navigating in the bit world still remains constrained by our limited thinking of real-world geometry. Hyperlinks were one useful step but are inadequate for the mountains of data we now have to navigate. VR and multimedia environments help a little, but they are still far too restricted for any really significant advance. It looks as though we need a breakthrough in geographic representation, and something that translates the multidimensional bit world back to our limited human abilities and concepts. There are some cues we can take from the fact that information networks and complexity are evolving to somewhat mimic our carbon-based wetware. Perhaps we should just let go of the notion of organizing information and let it do its own thing.

We never worry about the location of information and memories in our heads, we just request and it is retrieved, or withheld, at will. To some extent this is now true of the net. Do we really care where the server is located anymore? Mostly we just get a page on the screen from somewhere and go. Granted, there is a formal process that has some structure, but after that, the process and geography are totally invisible to us. Shortly, voice activation will make it even moreso; only delay will give any inference of virtual distance or complexity.

78

*"Money is a
poor man's credit card."*
Marshall McLuhan (1971)

BANKING BEYOND THE MUSEUM

While visiting a living museum recently, I stepped into a reconstructed Victorian bank. In the gloom of dark-stained wood was a huge metal safe, ledgers, scales, coinage, and the manager in starched collar. It all had that fossilized stability I remember from my childhood, and I began to reflect on the rate of change. I cannot remember the last time I saw anyone depositing a blue bag in a night safe, or having coins weighed. I presume it still happens. But then like many people, I seldom visit banks. Telephone banking and cash machines have become my lifeline.

The embodiment of change is perhaps exemplified by the acceleration of business, as coins, paper, and checks have been sidelined by plastic, and soon, electronic cash. Since the introduction of plastic, we reached a point where money = information = bits. So there is a direct analogy with the blue bag and the night safe. Businesses are at risk because their data is at risk. A stolen PC, fire damage, or disc crash can debilitate a business if the data is not backed up. So perhaps we need data banking in the broader sense.

Many people are working harder under the increasing competition driven by technological change. There is no time for decorating, gardening, or car cleaning. Curiously, they often pay more attention to their company accounts than their domestic situations. An effective solution is to outsource all personal financial management, with provisions for pension and insurance for the unforeseen. We are moving toward a more complex world of rapidly changing fortunes, job changing, and, for most of us, multiple employers. Thirty years ago a professional might have expected to work for three employers in a lifetime. Today, it is in excess of seven, and in 20 years it will be in excess of 25. Managing the tax, pension, insurance, and stability of such a life could be a nightmare without electronic outsourcing.

Looking around for a contemporary example, I found a young lady who graduated, worked for 18 months in a major company, and then went freelance. Her current and multiple simultaneous employers will total 35 by year's end. Who should she turn to for assistance and management? She needs a bank with all the data and expertise at hand so this growing problem can be reduced to a software package. She needs real-time business management as much as a company.

The addition of video conferencing and iris scanning customer identification and verification to the modest cash machines of today could conceivably render them virtual banks. And this technology could be extended directly into the home and office PC or laptop. No doubt bank branches will survive, but their nature can be expected to change dramatically, with more terminals than staff. But their primary function may remain real people contact, necessary when situations are too complex to fix by telephone, keyboard, or conference call. They may also become the intermediaries for the IT disabled.

Any form of computer terminal, electronic kiosk, or on-line organizer will potentially provide access to the many functions and services that necessitate a visit to a bank. What, then, will be the nature and skills of future bankers? Without a doubt, they will have to be IT capable and specialized in particular market sectors. Teams of advisors, experts, and mentors on-line will be necessary to deal with an increasingly sophisticated customer base living faster and more complex lives. They may also become road warriors, tracking and visiting customers wherever they happen to be, branches on wheels, in effect.

79

*Discontent is the
first step in the progress
of a man or a nation.*
Oscar Wilde (1854-1900)

CONCRETE AND CHIPS

As a young man I used to watch Stirling Moss push his racing car to the limit. There he sat, bolt upright behind a large steering wheel, with an engine mounted on a chassis carried on tall thin wheels and an up-front family saloon-style radiator. How differently today Damon Hill lies behind a tiny steering wheel, most of his body and engine below the axis of low and wide wheels. More radical—and unseen—is the absence of any chassis, now supplanted by the engine and drive chain, augmented by a distributed cooling and ventilation system.

During my early engineering education, I attended courses in materials, thermodynamics, and structures in which the design of efficient machines such as cars, aircraft, and electronic systems was addressed. It was something of a surprise to discover that bridge design also had useful aspects, either directly or by analogy to electronics. In my experience reinforced concrete does not excite many people. But it turns out to be pretty subtle stuff, of a complex chemistry, with hundreds of grades that vary the sand, cement, aggregate, and reinforcing mix. A vast range of properties can be realized by using everything from passive wire to tensioned steel ropes, pea shingle to rock chippings.

Testing a new laptop recently, I began to reflect on these past experiences when the battery got so hot it began to burn my leg, and it was so heavy it was stretching my arm. So I dismantled this virgin box to inspect the basic engineering. By any standard, it was nicely designed and produced, but the chunky CD and floppy drive plus battery pack consumed some 85 percent of the total base volume. The actual PC processing board and backup battery looked almost lonely sitting right there in the middle. My mind then turned to how it might be improved. The plastic case contained a metal support chassis, with a single mother board spread across the entire surface to provide the printed wiring interconnections between modules. So it occurred to me that given the inherent reliability of our chip and battery technologies, it might be worth considering a complete integration of electronics, thermal dissipation, and physical strength.

Heat dissipation could easily be improved by distributing the battery across the entire base, thereby more than quadrupling the surface area for dissipation, and stop it burning my leg. An amalgam of metalized foils, dielectric, printed wiring, and chips would have similar properties to the steel rods and aggregate in reinforced concrete. Moreover, these component parts would eliminate the need for a chassis as they became the integral strength in the structure. At a modest estimate the base thickness could be reduced by 60 percent and the overall weight by 20 percent. Including the plastic molding for the keyboard into the structure along with a passive mouse would offer more savings. Turning to the lid, to make any significant savings here would require an integrated backlit LCD and sound system that does not exist yet. However, the base technologies to do it are available. It is feasible.

If the notebook format computer is going to be a long-lived paradigm, then some new and radical steps are needed to advance the art. Although plug-in, modular building-block engineering is attractive, it increasingly looks inappropriate for a technology with an economic half-life of less than three years and an operational half-life greater than seven. The last time we did something like this, it severely limited a civilization. The Romans dissipated themselves building one bridge when they could have realized ten by pouring concrete instead of cutting stone.

80

*"I think we can safely assume
that no one understands
quantum mechanics."*

Richard Feynman (1966)

QUANTUM BITS

Just over 20 years ago I was coopted onto a team investigating the future of computer architecture. This was at a time when the mainframe ruled supreme and the minicomputer was just arriving on the scene. The futility of the task soon became apparent, as almost all the thinking was locked into a serial-digital mindset. It seemed to me that parallelism and a dash of uncertainty, or even a return to analogue processing, were key contenders for the future. Unable to sway the thinking process, I retired gracefully with the words, "Don't be surprised if we are growing computers in jam jars by the end of the millennium."

More recently, I was bombarded by e-mail and letters when I suggested that today's secure coding and encryption systems might be short-lived. This I proposed on the basis of them inevitably being overtaken by computing power that will unlock their secrets. We also seem to have developed a predominantly microprocessor mindset. This is despite the fact that Colossus, the WWII Bletchley Park code-cracking computer, is still far faster than a power PC at its specific class of codes. An architecturally task-specific machine always wins against a general machine running specific task-orientated software. But almost all of the >12Bn microprocessors on the planet (over twice as many as people) fall into the latter category. Only recently has the cost of cutting silicon rivaled that of cutting code, thereby allowing significant performance enhancements.

Suppose we had a technology that could do everything, a machine that could examine all the options. Well, it now looks as though a quantum computer is feasible. If we could use the states of elemental particles such as electrons and protons as analogues of today's transistors, we could get all the world's computing power today in a jam jar of fluid. The biggest stride forward would be the ability to examine all paths, states, and solutions simultaneously. This would be possible because particles have a quantum nature, with states defined by spin or dispersed location.

It is amusing to see how the term "quantum leap" has been distorted by the media to imply a giant change. In reality a quantum leap is an infinitesimal, almost unmeasurable change, and presents a major realization challenge for quantum computing. Detecting the changes of state looks to be fundamentally tricky. Recently, a quantum computer calculated $1 + 1 = 2$, not very impressive but very important. This was the transition to reality of a dream coined in 1985 by Richard Feynman. The prediction is that a practicable quantum computer will be with us in another 10 or so years, and perhaps on our desks 10 years later. If this turns out to be true, it will give us undreamed of computing abilities. What would we do with such power?

I think almost all of the outstanding classical mathematical and physical science problems could be solved in minutes by such machines. No doubt, we could also enhance our ability to predict the weather, markets, network, and business activity. Perhaps the key contribution such power might afford would be the ability to model people, society, and change. Instead of being subject to the chaotic change invoked by technology, perhaps we could get ahead of the game and back in the decision loop, to exercise a sensible and timely steer. We might even find ourselves able to educate people for the future, as opposed to educating them for the past as we do today.

81

*"Life is too short
for a long story."*
Lady Mary Wortley Montagu (1759)

AN E-MAIL IS NOT A LETTER

Working across a broad front of industry, commerce, education, government, and technology, I get to visit and work inside many organizations across the planet. Although some are more advanced than others, all are struggling to keep up and keep ahead. Among the most common management complaints are those related to e-mail overload. Quantity is often cited as the key problem, but I suspect it is more a matter of relevance, style, and common sense.

Only one generation ago paper proliferation was promoted by the photocopier, and everyone got a copy in parallel, just in case they needed to know. The generation before that relied on carbon copies and traveling files. Triplication of a typed original was easy, but beyond that carbon paper rapidly becomes faint. So the traveling file on circulation for days and weeks was the adopted mode in this staid past.

In an e-mail world there is a carbon paper equivalent. CC = carbon copy, and Bcc = blind carbon copy. The problem appears to be that people love CC, and they electronically copy to everyone. But unlike carbon, electronic copies are as good as the original, and unlimited. I have seen messages simultaneously copied to 400 or more people. If only the protagonists would discover Bcc, then the 400 line address header would be invisible and the message shorter and more accessible. If you are working on the move using a mobile or fixed telephone line with a low-bit-rate modem, it is extremely inconvenient and time-consuming to download all this irrelevant information.

E-mail is positioned somewhere between a telegram and a formal letter, far more communicative than the former, but far less formal than the latter. Among the worst practices I have seen are the full blown formal business letters with header, footer, Dear Sir/Madam, and Yours Sincerely, copied into the E-mail page, or worse, copied as an attachment. This is another inconvenient and unnecessary practice. It's a waste of everyone's time writing, reading, downloading, decoding, and sometimes finding that you cannot translate from the sender's obscure word processing package.

E-mail is about communicating fast and efficiently. It was developed during the initial stages of the Internet when pipes were narrow and computers slow, and it is intentionally informal, free from the constraints established by the paper past and Dickensian mind-sets. This is certainly not a verbose and flowery medium. If only the originators of all communication would be considerate to their audiences and desist from wearing their eyes out with unnecessary words, not to mention bombarding everyone with irrelevant stuff just because it is easy to do. As a general rule, the value of any document or communication is inversely proportional to its length and weight. In general, quantity seldom equates to quality.

In the converse direction there is also the out-of-context syndrome. Having communicated once, people often suffer under the illusion that they have established an exclusive channel to your brain. A message appears mentioning Fred and a meeting next Monday without any context. If only the sender would append the original communication as a traveling file, life would be so much easier. Having to search all your files for a hint of Fred is really no fun at all.

People have different personas in the flesh, on the screen and telephone, and certainly in the handwritten and typed letter. They also behave differently at home, work, and play. The e-world offers a further degree of freedom that ought not to be infected by the bad or irrelevant practices of the dead world of the quill pen.

82

*"There is no private life
which has not been
determined by a
wider public life."*

George Eliot (1866)

EYES EVERYWHERE

We have all become acquainted with the privacy-invading photographers and their love of the rich and famous as their primary victims. Well, technology now offers us all the opportunity to be amateur paparazzi and victims at the same time. We may have our very own 15 Mbytes of fame, like it or not. Just cast an eye around any street or store to see the obvious— and not so obvious—range of security cameras. And then there is Joe Public sporting the latest handheld camcorder or digital camera. We are heading toward a world where we can all be voyeurs and victims.

The glass wall of my office allows anyone walking by to see me at any time. To augment this, I installed a camera I named Little Brother to allow anyone anywhere to look in at anytime. I see it as just another window. At first I had a chime to alert me that someone was looking, this being a parallel of my being aware of the presence of people. The prospect of such a facility alarmed many colleagues, and even moreso when I removed the chime. Generally, people do not like the prospect of always being on public view.

This was carried out as an experiment to see what advantage could be realized by being able to drop into someone's office at will. Are they in, on their own, free or busy? This is useful information in a world that is speeding up, and we are increasingly short of time. Interestingly, some of my people reciprocated with even more little brother cameras and widely varying degrees of commitment to always being on view.

Provided this is a matter of personal choice and we are individually in control, I can see little objection to such systems.

What should we be worrying about? Is there some underlying threat posed by a technology providing an ability to place miniature cameras in and on anything? Being on camera and being aware of the fact, even if it is an unconscious awareness, is one thing, but the spy camera is another. The next time you are in a hotel, elevator, shopping center, office block, car park, anywhere, seek out the cameras and ask the fundamental question: Do I feel threatened or comforted, exposed or safe? Most people see them as a safety feature and a comfort. This is perhaps a counterintuitive outcome promoted by their success in crime prevention and solution. Even speed cameras on roads and the eye-in-the-sky helicopter have been quietly accepted by the public at large as providing more benefit than threat. After receiving a speeding ticket, most are reasonably ambivalent; it was a fair cop, and I shouldn't have been driving so fast.

Where do we draw the line? At what point do we react against this creeping invasion of our individual activities? For me, it is the concealed cameras smaller than a shirt button worn as jewelry or embedded in some obscure inanimate object, when I am totally unaware of the user and the purpose. I for one do not wish to live in a world where my thinking, actions, and speech become constrained by the threat of being on record for later unspecified use, in or out of context. The technology is available, and it is being used. Legal agencies using the technology is one thing, but not individuals, corporations, the media, and others. I vote that cameras in these sectors be made very visible when active.

83

"Every political system is an accumulation of habits, customs, prejudices, and principles that have survived a long process of trial and error . . . "

Edward C. Banfield (1989)

ELECTRONIC ELECTION

Here we are almost in the new millennium still scratching crosses on paper and counting people like sheep. Political process seems to be out of kilter with society and technological progress, and obsolete in terms of future national wealth creation. While the management and processes of companies are continually honed by competition, and a need to become more efficient, the management of countries continues as if it were still the 1600s. Electronic banking, commerce, and income tax returns are visible proof of due change. How long can country management afford to maintain ancient traditions and practices? Well, until there is some form of competition or pressure, change is unlikely. But there is a growing danger that politicians and establishments will increasingly be sidelined by a high speed world of electronic commerce.

A month before the UK electorate shuffled down to the voting booths to make their mark, a virtual general election was held on the net, with students at 67 schools voting at the press of a key. Interestingly, the difference between the actual and virtual election was <30 percent. Not bad for such a small sample. I haven't tried to estimate how much could be saved by dispensing with the paper process and going electronic, but it must be millions. Obviously, if all countries stick to paper and tradition, the status quo will prevail, but look out for the first to break the mold and decide to move faster.

Looking at the political assemblies of nations, it is hard to imagine how the decision making and voting processes of old can survive into the 21st century. Our world is speeding up, and so is the need for faster understanding and appreciation of complex situations. In military circles war gaming is a vital tool for training and honing the skills of the individual and the whole. Gradually, this is also becoming the case for business, with computer modeling of markets and decision plays prior to the real encounter. It is likely that the future of commerce will be highly dependent on a meld of human and machine intelligence honed by prior practice.

Before the Gulf War a vast number of scenarios had been played out by commanders and strategists. Every move and action had been anticipated in this multiple partner conflict. What was not anticipated, however, was the actual speed of progress, which ran well ahead of the modelers' ability to input into the games machines. This was only possible in retrospect, and did not envelope the political dimension. Here the focus was on logistics and damage alone. Fortunately, for the present, business is not so reactive and fast. Real-time updates are still possible. And so models track reality and provide predictions in almost real time. Politics, on the other hand, is far slower, but also far more complex than commerce or tactical warfare.

When confronted with the overcomplex, we almost always revert to simplification and thereby build a gap between understanding, truth, and reality. In warfare this can return terrible results, but it seems modeling has reached the level of sophistication necessary to effectively close this gap. In business lives are not lost, but livelihoods can be, and electronic modeling and war gaming is only now emerging as a valued tool. As for politics, which has the ability to create widespread wealth or poverty, we have yet to make any significant inroads. For the first time we have the mechanism to instantly measure the mood of populations and hand each individual a franchise on the management of his or her nation. If we do not, then we should not be surprised if their allegiance and focus of attention become redirected.

84

THE BABEL BUG

Given the rapidly growing number of computer operating systems and languages, it seems likely there will be a future demand for translator programs. Our species has created a world of Babel—no one standard language, and we now seem to be avidly repeating the exercise in IT. There are at least ten major operating systems for mainframes, PCs, palmtops, and PDAs. The electronic diary, mobile phone, calculator, engine management system, TV, and hi-fi represent a further rapidly expanding list. But if all systems are to become a community of electronic capability, how are they to communicate when a single language or operating system looks increasingly unlikely?

How about virus technology? Could an electronic virus enter a machine, look for data matches, decode the logic, unpick and understand MSDoS, Mac OS, or OS-2, W-CE, and Unix for starters? Well, perhaps, and if connected to a network, it might even move between machines making comparisons to realize a universal translator. Suddenly, network would talk to network, machine to machine, appliance to appliance, and device to device, all seamlessly. What a breakthrough.

Whoever creates such a technology will render the world a great service. Companies could then merge, as their disparate networks, machines, applications, databases, and programs would interwork. Logistic, operational, and financial optimization would then be possible on a global scale. In addition, individuals would find all machines, networks, and databases accessible with ease. All electronic entities could be addressed, programmed, and controlled. What a boon. At last everything would interwork, no more error messages and calls for extra software installation by the genie of the net.

As new systems came on-line the virus would invade, learn, grow, and provide evermore links. But soon our world would be dependent on a singular item of software. Would there be a significant downside to this? Well, I reckon the "Babel bug" would soon be on the critical path of our very survival.

No doubt the originators would be canny and cash in on this miracle of technology and the electronic freedom they bestow on the population of the planet. But would they be greedy? Would they seek to control and manipulate the world as the dominant moguls do today? I think the temptation would be too great to resist. And all they have to do is build in a back door control access to the bug. Charge people for each translation, with the threat of no more as soon as they fail to pay the bill, and an infinite revenue stream is assured, the world is ransomed at a fraction of a penny a go.

And then? No doubt about it, bug wars would follow. First, there would come the competition, the technology followers. When it is possible, and that may be soon, you will not have to be a genius to realize a really smart bug. So competing virus translators will be released onto the net in the spirit of competition. Most likely someone will then originate a seek, find, and destroy virus to gain a bigger market share, and we have a new form of germ warfare. This would put us all at risk because in this regard our technological society really does depend more on technology than people.

In the worst case we could expect the bug moguls to build in software bombs to be activated when they expire by unnatural means. Their intent? To realize a deterrent to physical attack by reeking IT havoc in retribution. Perhaps then we will need an immune mechanism for the net, good bugs to fight the bad.

85

FINGERS AND BUTTONS

For reasons buried in my genetic past, I was born with large hands and fingers. Today, I wear a wedding ring of Z+ size and my hands are a valuable asset in any ball game. But these great sausages for digits also cause me a deal of technology trouble. Many of our modern devices seem to have been designed with only the genteel and dainty in mind. On most pocket calculators, personal organizers, mobile phones, radio, TV, VHS, and hi-fi controllers, I can hit three or four buttons at once. And as for the dreaded multifunction digital wristwatch, I have to resort to the tip of a pen or a pin. It feels as if the most basic of human dimensions are now being overlooked by designers.

The variation in the position of the human eyes, ears, and mouth have been characterized over decades for many thousands of people, and their distribution is known with precision. The mobile phone, however, is becoming progressively smaller and shorter, with the microphone gradually migrating away from the mouth toward the ear. Despite claims to the contrary of the manufacturers, this is responsible for a progressive reduction in the acoustic performance of these devices. I for one will not undergo plastic surgery to have my lips surgically moved to the middle of my cheek.

More recently, all of this has been augmented by palmtop computers, pagers, cameras, and many other devices that display individual icons and characters so small that many people have to resort to a magnifying glass. What is happening and why make such user-unfriendly technology?

The reality is that almost every item of technology we commonly use and carry can be reduced to a single chip, or at most three, on a single printed circuit board. Screens, keyboards, and batteries dominate the physical realization and dictate the ultimate dimensions. This is further compounded by the pressure on manufacturing costs to use a minimum of raw material. Obviously, this line of development cannot be sustained indefinitely; we must do something new and different.

One obvious solution is to coalesce several devices into one large unit and thereby reduce the total number of buttons, knobs, and screens, while realizing sufficient surface area for a reasonable scale. The combined pager, mobile phone, personal assistant, and network computer can, initially at any rate, be a human-scale device. We can also adopt voice interaction and new head up displays, but the trend of minimization will continue apace. Perhaps a more attractive route would be to disassociate the interface from the device. A keyboard, keypad, mouse, screen, microphone, or speaker unit that can drive or be driven by anything would be a real boon. This would be especially so if terminals were available everywhere, and we could personalize and configure this highly personal unit to meet our specific needs. Moreover, for streets and public places, such a solution would drastically reduce the opportunities for vandals.

There is also at least one other comfort that such a technology would bring us, and that is manipulative familiarity, or old-shoe syndrome. Instead of finding ourselves pressured into committing unnatural acts of finger geometry every time we buy a new device, we could stick with our hard-won and long-standing routines.

As technology advances at an accelerating pace, it is unreasonable of designers to ask the population to learn four or five new interfaces every year. Like the automobile, IT will have to stabilize for commonly used devices and adopt some limiting conventions. And this should include usable buttons and displays.

86

"What vast additions to the conveniences and comforts of living might mankind have acquired, if the money spent in wars had been employed in works of public utility . . . "

Benjamin Franklin (1783)

BITS = BULLETS?

It is an unfortunate but inescapable fact that the most dramatic surges in human technological progress have historically been stimulated by war or the perceived threat of some major conflict. In the modern arena, no one could be but impressed by the cold and deadly precision of the intelligent weapons used in the Gulf War: bombs dispatched from fast-moving aircraft not merely hitting the target but entering by a designated window or ventilation shaft; cruise missiles that actively compared their own internal maps with the scanned terrain to deliver their deadly cargo of high explosives.

It is fair to say that the advance in weapons and systems of war probably requires no specific enhancement beyond what is already being done. It continues apace because it is extremely competitive. The army with the most effective weapons wins. Logistics, however, continues to be a nightmare for both military and civilian operations alike.

What might be done? Well, consider the prospect of everything on-line, a world of "intelligent things" having circuits addressable by radio. Having every item of weaponry, shell, bullet, article of clothing, and kit on-line would revolutionize delivery, support, and maintenance. This is already being done experimentally for civilian applications and could soon become a feature of the retail marketplace. Extensive effort is now being expended to reduce the checkout lines and the inconvenience of having to wait, plus the costly errors and losses in transport and deliv-

ery. On the battlefield we might contemplate commanders able to identify disabled weapons and machinery, diagnose the failure, and then
locate a similar kit that can be cannibalized to effect a rapid repair. The
logistical implications for all sectors are obviously profound.

In any high tech operation getting repairs made is becoming
increasingly critical. In the civilian world having customers off-line due
to equipment failures is inexcusable, and extremely expensive. The failure of network links can see millions of dollars lost in a very short time.
Replacement components need locating fast. In the military context it
is not money and collateral damage that dominate the equation, but
the loss of human life. Being able to communicate with everyone is the
first step toward a modern and efficient military machine; the second is
being able to talk to everything, to keep the machinery of warfare
rolling. To date, experiments have been completed with single chips
powered by small batteries and passive units addressed and powered
by radios implanted in clothing and weapons.

A similar series of experiments have shown the office and hospital
you were to be close to practical realization. The abilities of the laptop
and mobile phone reduced to body-mounted units along with medical monitors and automated drug dispensers are just a first step.
Prototypes can now monitor over 10 vital life signs and relay them back
to some distant hospital or GP. Ultimately, they will also administer life-
supporting medicines from afar. Perhaps more impressively, artificial
clothing layers that sense injury and then perform limited treatment
and repair of human subjects also looks to be possible. Callous as it may
seem, in the military arena, knowing that someone is dead, about to
die, or beyond all help could save lives by minimizing the number of
futile attempts at rescue under dangerous conditions.

For commanders in the field this all translates into the ultimate chess
board. For the first time they will be able to see the status of every person, weapon, and bullet. They will also be able to optimize rescue, repair,
and response. But most importantly, they will be able to see more and
react faster than the enemy. Bullets and bits may then be equal.

87

"Love, by its very nature,
is unworldly, and . . .
the most powerful of all . . .
human forces . . . "

Hannah Arendt (1958)

THINKING OF YOU

Like many people who continually travel, I always carry a selection of pictures of my wife and children. These automatically appear on my laptop as part of my screensaver function, and I can also manually pull up pictures to decorate my hotel room or office wherever I might be. Like the paper versions I no longer carry, these provide a level of home comfort and augment my e-mail and telephone conversations. I always find it rather nice and somehow reassuring to look at a picture of wife and children as I talk to them from some distant location.

I also seem to find myself thinking of my family during the inevitable lulls in meetings and conferences, and while traveling by air, train, and car. Mostly, I resort to gently turning the wedding ring on my left hand as I contemplate recent days at home, or, more frequently, days to come at the end of a trip. It was this almost unconscious habit that prompted me to contemplate the prospect of communicating jewelry. The wristwatch phone is with us, and soon it may become a badge or a brooch. How reassuring it would be if moving my wedding ring resulted in a gentle "thinking of you" movement of my wife's ring, wristwatch, bracelet, or earrings, and vice versa. How comforting it would be to realize a degree of invisible tactile communication between family members.

If the simplest of pagers can be programmed to vibrate and give a visual readout every time Manchester United scores a goal or Barbados takes another wicket in the West Indies, or give urgent news updates, why can't they provide emotional connections to our loved ones? The technology realization is straightforward enough and may even prove irresistible once available. At last, we could always be in touch, literally.

Another travel-related service I would appreciate is on-line real time views of my home from cameras in the garden and drive. After all there are cameras on the net showing coffee pots, motorway junctions, airports, people's living rooms, and even a few bedrooms by subscription. So why not my house? Just think of the personal reassurance potential. Is my house still there, has there been any storm damage, how is the painter progressing, where did that ball go through the window? The applications and opportunities for emotional reassurance seem endless.

Of course, this could be extended to other inanimate objects too. Chips and cameras in cars can now detect a thief, take a series of photographs, activate a radio system to alert the police, and provide a tracking beacon so the culprit can be apprehended in the act. By simply connecting the mobile phone to a Global Positioning System we could locate vehicles almost anywhere on the planet, including the car park when we have forgotten where we parked several hours before. I for one would like my car to flash it's lights and sound the horn so I can find it. I would also like a remote run down on the status of my vehicle on my way back to an airport, and be able to disable it if stolen. I would also like access to the burglar and fire alarm of my home, and the personal safety alarms of family members—in fact, why not every human I care for, and every artifact I purchase and value?

No doubt, some people will balk at this prospect on the basis of the big brother image. But all the evidence points to such technology giving us even greater freedom and a new route to a rather more relaxed life.

88

*"First come hints,
then fragments of systems,
then defective systems,
then complete and harmonious systems."*

Thomas Babington Macaulay (1835)

OPERATING SYSTEM WARS

Just when it seemed that operating system wars were over, and we all looked to be doomed to a monotonic life on a singular and constraining platform, along comes Java. Might this put an en to the OS2, Mac, MSoft, Windows, et al. arm-wrestling contest, and all the emotional reaction that ensues, over what are increasingly marginal differences? No one knows or can predict the final fate of Java. It could become the universal programming language and a bridge across a growing environment of multiple operating systems. At the very least, network computing with Java looks set to take off in corporate markets, where bandwidth is not a cost concern to the individual and up-to-date information is a key to competitive success. Also, it seems reasonable that hybrids, halfway houses between the NC and PC, will also emerge. Even mother nature did not put all the brains and information in the heads of animals. She distributed it around the body, and for very good reason.

Exchanging bandwidth for memory is something that people do not readily understand or care to contemplate. One is assumed expensive and the other cheap. Ask someone at random what the cost of bit transport is, a phone call, for example, and they will estimate between three and five times too high. On the other hand, they are very likely to be able to tell you the price of a CD, audio, or video tape. More interestingly, most of us spend far more on CDs and tapes than phone calls. People just do not seem to appreciate bandwidth, its value, or its future role. For the most part it costs next to nothing relative to everything else we consume, and almost all other IT features can therefore be traded against raw bit transport. Data compression, storage, reliability, and latency are all obvious targets.

Today, information bottlenecks are everywhere. The protocols and interfaces within computers and networks are based on old and long-gone copper technologies. Optical fiber can deliver more bandwidth than the human mind can imagine. While commercial networks are generally constrained to less than 10 Gbit/s, experimental systems are now exceeding 100 Gbit/s and ultimately should pass well beyond 1 Tbit/s per fiber. But do not expect such bandwidth delivered to the top of Mount Everest or the wilds of Montana, or even in a London street. Ultimately, fixed-fiber cables will deliver capacity to hubs with twisted pair, coax, fiber, radio, and optical wireless access.

Think of walking into an office block to find 1 Gbit/s delivered by an optical link, or 10 Mbit/s in a restaurant via 90 GHz radio, 2 Mbit/s at the railway station by short hop radio, 9.6 kbit/s by GSM on the highway, 100 Mbit/s at the service station, 2.4 kbit/s by satellite in the middle of a desert, and so on. Bandwidth is practically unlimited on fiber and radio because the full spectrum has yet to be exploited. Specifically, the radio spectrum remains mostly untapped above 30 GHz, where frequency reuse is a natural option afforded by rapidly increasing atmospheric absorption restricting communication distance.

So who cares? What we really need is true plug and play and invisible operating systems that allow us to run a raft of competitive applications purposely made compatible and not exclusively restricting. By default, processing will be everywhere and effective computing will see chips in everything from the door knob to clothing, jewels, automobiles, washing machines, pacemakers, and more. For the future to work bit processing and storage has to be everywhere. It cannot be centralized, and it cannot be singular or operating system centric. Java may turn out to be a vital step in this direction.

89

RISK EXPERTS

Take a sheet of graph paper ruled with 1/32-inch small squares and assign one day of human life to each square. On that page is represented more time than we can reasonably expect to live. After three score years and ten we have consumed some 25,550 days, and only about 70 percent of the squares. This is 613,200 hours, or 36,792,000 minutes. When viewed on a single side of paper, our lifetime seems short, especially when it takes us about 30 percent of the total to mature and become proficient at anything significantly useful.

Numbers and physical space are often deceptive and elusive quantities. More than one ancient tribe adopted numbering schemes that only spanned one, two, and sufficient.

Yet in our modern world we have to come to terms with multidimensional statistics and data spanning the infinitesimally small to the astronomically large.

When assimilating information, we are naturally inclined to the analogue rather than the digital, especially when it is incidental and has to be done at a glance. Witness the rise and fall of the digital watch and car speedometer, for example. Modern aircraft are a delightful mix of both analogue and digital displays for very good reason. While in a car the precision of the fuel and oil pressure gauge can be approximate, that's not true in an aircraft where lives are at stake. When precision is required, we generally have to resort to digital formats.

Almost every week there seems to be some new major risk to worry us. Taking the contraceptive pill regularly increases your risk of thrombosis threefold. Eating or drinking certain products reduces your chances of reaching retirement by x percent. These and similar are typical of headline scare stories. But quoted out of context such figures are meaningless and grossly misleading. Three times a very small number is still a very small number. For example, the risk of death from mad cow disease (CJD) is at worst about 1 in 5,000,000, and at best 1 in 500,000,000. But the use of contraceptive pills is at least 100 times riskier at 1 in 50,000, and alcohol-induced liver failure is around 1 in 18,000. Worse still, traffic accidents present a 1 in 7000 chance of being killed, While smoking cigarettes is 1 in 200. If you are simultaneously exposed to such risks, then CJD is insignificant, even less of a threat than salmonella poisoning from poultry.

Of course, there are always a vast range of the variables involved in estimating risk. How much beef, how often, purchased from where, prepared and eaten under what conditions? As the disease has been on record since the middle ages, perhaps we should also worry about the eating habits of our parents.

When we only had paper, it was excusable to present statistics badly, but we now have computers and there is really no excuse. Curiously, we use IT to a very high degree for explaining the outcomes and implications of political elections, sporting events, entertainment quiz shows, and other trivia. But when it comes to the complex issues that impact our future, we resort to gross and meaningless simplifications like, "the risk has increased threefold."

Fortunately, it is possible to get a more balanced and worthwhile view. While the established media hypes and sensationalizes information and thereby gets the message wrong, the raw information, often complete with graphics, is usually available on the net. All you have to do is search, examine, and think. Soon we may also gain access to the models used by the experts to formulate their opinions. We will all then be as expert as the experts, and ahead of the media.

90

"I was taught that the human brain was the crowning glory of evolution so far, but I think it's a very poor scheme for survival."

Kurt Vonnegut (1987)

SILICON IQ

Many years ago I worked on radio system design when the distance between transmitter sites was measured in miles, the tower height was in feet, parabolic dish diameter in cm, and frequency in cycles per second, field strength was in mV/m, and wind force in pounds per square inch. What a nightmare of units, manipulation, and potential for error.

Before the introduction of the metric (SI) system, technologists faced a major hurdle of communication with the arbitrary use of feet and meters, ounces and grams, Celsius and Fahrenheit, slugs, dynes, and more. Progress and thinking were fundamentally limited by the need to convert everything into an understandable form. Today, disparate groups from different disciplines can comprehend the Newton, Kelvin and Watt. This unified language of time, space, action, and energy has been fundamentally responsible for much technological progress over the past 30 years.

Now we face a new and more important challenge. How can we meaningfully rate computer power? We currently cite Millions of Instructions Per Second (MIPS) or Floating Point Operations per Second (FLOPS), with raw, formatted, and compressed information. There is no general way to make measurements or accurate comparisons. Extending this to non-serial, non-digital computers, animals and humans we seem even worse off, and reduced to making the best estimates we can based on problem solving parallels.

Probably the most commonly used measure for carbon systems is the Intelligence Quotient (IQ) test based upon the time to solve a range

of problems under test conditions. In reality this only gives an aggre-
gated measure of the ability to solve a class of problems relative to a
test population. It is on this basis that our species looks pretty smart,
at the top of the class, because we thought up the problems in the first
place. In a way this is an unfair and incomplete and unfair technique.
If rats and monkeys set IQ tests we might find ourselves further down
the league table for agility, finding food, a mate, and reproducing for
example.

Compared to machines we are obviously outclassed on production
lines, navigation, numerical computation, chess, and much more. Yet
we only have the conversational Touring Test as a notional measure of
human-machine equivalence. Worse still, we are instinctively dismissive
of "intelligent machines"—something we never do to our own species no
matter how seriously damaged. Perhaps it would be more sensible to
derive a comprehensive measure from problem class evaluations. We
could then say that; machines assemble camcorders 1000 times faster
than us; sort letters 100 times faster; are better than the best of us at
chess, calculate 1000,000,000 times faster, but recognize a face, pen, or
a cup of coffee with only 0.001 times our precision. On such a basis we
could have a running comparison of silicon and carbon systems, and
most importantly a true measure of their relative abilities. This would not
only give a clearer picture of machine progress, it might also help allay
techno-fear and provide a steer for future investment and development.

If we play a game of plugging in numbers; I reckon that the average machine- to -human ratio for a limited range of activities is of the
order: Numerical manipulation = 10EXP9:1, Games = 1:1, Motor precision
= 10EXP3:1, Bit communication = 10EXP7:1, Artifact and voice recognition = 1:10EXP4, Ambulating = 1:10EXP4, and so on. This is impressive—
just aggregating all these factors would rate machines ∼10EXP8 smarter
than humans. But this is a limited subset, and if I included Imagination
= Love = Feeling = Intuition = Many More = <<0.1, then machines are seriously disadvantaged, and we still win.

91

"Newspapers are unable, seemingly, to discriminate between a bicycle accident and the collapse of civilization."

George Bernard Shaw (1931)

HAVE I GOT NEWS FOR ME

A recent car accident dominated all newspapers, magazines, radio, and TV broadcasts for well over a week. A single death invoked total news chaos in one country and more or less dominated the world news. At the extreme of the reporting frenzy, one American TV presenter was heard to say, "We are probably witnessing the single biggest tragedy of the 20th century." What? A tragic loss of life, yes, but what about the countless thousands of people who died unnoticed during the same period or in the many wars of the past or of the last decade alone? What is happening, and why this extraordinary focus?

It seems that the media and the populations they influence are now well into an "all or nothing" world of strange and very strange attractors that chaotically pull the attention of the majority onto one topic. Single-issue politics has been overtaken by single-issue news, the passive following of a preselected and prepared daily raft of information. But no one seems to worry, and most do not seem to notice this global and singular bit-feed tempered by copy sales and audience ratings. In contrast, many people are apparently worried about the evils of the Internet. Is this rational? Could it possibly be worse?

News is now big business. If there is no news, then it has to be found or manufactured, and it has to be either fun, sensational, or shocking. We have fixed-size newspapers and magazines, regular news slots on radio and TV, and all have to be filled with finite bytes. It seems they cannot be left blank or be filled with non-news material; these are exclusively news bytes. In a sensible world news would be of variable length, graded by importance, and ultimately focused on the needs and interests of individuals—you and me. But broadcast radio and TV and newspapers cannot do this. Only computer-driven services have the ability to create "The Daily Me."

What I would give to be free of all the radio, TV, and print newsfeeds that are so inefficient at delivering the very few bytes of interest, relevance, and use to me. Instead of wasting hours viewing, listening, and rummaging through the unwanted remains of some forest reconstituted and served up as paper, in what seems to be an increasingly vain expectation of finding something of real importance, I desire a truly personal bitfeed.

Push technologies and their derivatives give us the first glimmer of hope that a future of "The Daily Me" may just be possible. Electronic agents that roam the global network on our behalf looking for information that we would each appreciate on an individual basis are now almost with us. In this regime the news can be customized by individuals rather than organizations. So we will individually control and dictate what qualifies as news for us. We will judge the relevance.

One interesting result we might anticipate is the human population being categorized by interests and responses to news and information feeds selected. Suppose, then, you and I have similar interests and we independently register a series of requests and respond favorably to a given number of news items. It would be a simple matter indeed to identify a 70 percent correlation with others to form a given interest group. Then things I had accessed and you hadn't would constitute a likely favorable offering and vice versa. Just add a smidgen of serendipity, or directed randomness, and bingo, we can all have just the bits we need, no more, no less.

92

"In a digital world anything can be a fake, and a fake is as good as an original."

Anonymous

SHOPPING FOR ATOMS AND BITS

Take a good look in your home and car to search out all the old vinyl records, audiotapes, videos, and CDs. Then estimate the cubic capacity of storage space they require. It is not difficult to find that you have enough to fill at least one large suitcase and possibly two or more. While we worry, and quite rightly, about the overuse of paper and the destruction of trees, we might also be concerned by the conversion of hydrocarbons into plastic. Fortunately, the progression of electronic and optical data storage technology is riding an exponential wave, with massive increases in density and perhaps thereby a reduction in raw material usage per person overall.

If you want a surprise, just take the sale price of each of the items you have found and estimate the total. You will find it amounts to an amazingly high number, a significant investment. Another interesting exercise is to search out all the radios, record, tape, and CD players you own, in whatever format and condition. The result can also be a surprise. Most of us are awash with such technology—current, forgotten, and discarded. It has become so low-cost we can afford to have several of everything. Just work out the total purchase cost, and in general it is the software that represents (by far) the greatest proportion of this very personal investment.

Traveling abroad, it is interesting to see that the hardware to access these recorded bits, radios, tape, and CD players, are reasonably close in price across the globe. However, the software, tapes and CDs, presents a huge disparity, often in excess of 50 percent. We need not discuss the reasons here but merely observe that the soft sector is under threat from its own technology. The writeable CD is coming and with it a major opportunity for change. It will not only create the opportunity to reduce the cost of purchase, but also the desire to build our own ensemble of music and videos. That may be the greatest advance. I can never remember buying a CD or tape that contained my ideal choice of material. It is always a compromise.

In this new world we will be able to pull into the garage, fill up the tank with gasoline, and at the same time fill up the hi-fi with new music. An optical free space link to the car will see us filling up with bits, while a hose tops up the car with atoms. As we shop in a store, we could do the same bit collection while buying food or a newspaper. A future Walkman will have both a read and write capability, so why purchase a CD that is preburnt-in and fixed? Also, why retain the information in the Walkman or car hi-fi when you can download into the home hi-fi system? At this point shopping for bits starts to equate to shopping for atoms, except that there will be a radical drop in price. People may be prepared to pay a premium for a nice cardboard cover or plastic box but not, I suspect, for bits alone.

This technology should see many new points of sale and pickup fed by optical fiber so they can deliver 0.5 to 8 GByte of audio entertainment in just a few minutes. And then you and I, and our vehicles, may become the carriers, the new messengers, delivering bits to home and office. When we can all share information between bit storage units we carry or wear, each of us will become part of a new network of human bit couriers.

93

"Anyone who has ever looked into the glazed eyes of a soldier dying on the battlefield will think hard before starting a war."

Otto Von Bismarck (1867)

FRIENDLY FIRE

Friendly fire is a military euphemism for being shot by your own side. In any armed conflict there are all too often self-inflicted casualties through genuine mistakes, accidents, and panic. And worse, there is a high risk that civilians or innocent bystanders will be unintentionally hurt. Armies and police forces spend immense amounts of money training their people in the use of weapons and the avoidance of self-inflicted tragedies. Looking at the theater of modern conflicts and the capabilities of modern weapons, it is amazing that friendly fire does not account for an even higher proportion of the casualties.

Playing an energetic combat game with some children recently, it occurred to me that we had in the making a cure for friendly fire. The laser pistols and head-mounted target detectors now used in games could translate to a miniature laser unit mounted on a pistol, rifle, and other weapons. As the weapon is aimed, a uniquely coded burst of identifying photons could be launched at the human, vehicular, or other form of target. A receiver unit could then decode the photon message to respond with a unique friendly reply. Although light travels at 300,000,000 m/s, the pulses in our nervous system are vastly slower, and our reaction time is generally over 0.1 s. So the reply message could disable the weapon before the trigger finger could initiate a deadly release of munitions.

Thinking more broadly, it is clear that this concept is not entirely novel. Since WWII military aircraft have been fitted with IFF

(Identification Friend or Foe) so radar systems can remotely identify them. Today, IFF is essential for all military and commercial aircraft. But IFF is radio-based, relatively unfocused, and responds to radar pulses by generating a unique identifier signal by return. Of most importance to you and me, today's IFF systems allow for the efficient and safe management of air travel across the planet. In short, they prevent accidents. Knowing what type of aircraft, who owns it, and how fast and high it is traveling is vital in this arena.

No amount of intelligence information or people training by armies and police forces will eradicate the risk from friendly fire. But people, equipment, and weapons with highly localized optical IFF systems could reduce the problem significantly at very low cost relative to the loss of human life and trauma.

The question now arise: What about civilians, innocents, and unnecessary collateral damage? Beyond fitting everyone and everything with some neutral IFF system, which is open to abuse by combatants, there seems to be little that can be done. But at least on the military front we might expect that all sides in a conflict and all manufacturers of armaments would find it advantageous to adopt such technology. Those opting out would be seriously disadvantaged, and anyone stealing weapons from the opposing side would find them electronically locked and useless.

Clearly, the most dangerous time would be during a partial or one-sided deployment. This would potentially create a significant imbalance of firepower. Just pointing a gun in the general direction of an enemy and discharging thousands of rounds in the sure knowledge that your own side cannot be hit directly would imply a deskilling of troops. But when they do not have to hesitate, their reaction time would be significantly improved.

At this point, a further development would obviously follow, the remotely operated robotic camera gun. Why put yourself in the line of fire at all when a machine can take all the risks? Somehow, it feels as though RoboCop has just came a step closer to reality.

94

"Any sufficiently advanced technology is indistinguishable from magic."
Arthur C. Clarke (1987)

THE MOLECULE IS THE MESSAGE

When you are next at your computer, you might like to contemplate the storage and processing capabilities inside the box. You will probably assume this is to be dominated by magnetic, electronic, and photonic technology. Actually, you would be wrong. A single flake of dead skin falling from your scalp to embed itself between the keys would carry, and join, a huge population of living bacteria. Each bacterium can conservatively store and process upwards of 1–10 GBytes with individual enzyme matching in much less than 2 ms. This is both stunning and an indication of how far our technology has to go before we catch up with biological information processing and the evolutionary development of mother nature. At the present rate of progress, with a doubling of technology abilities every 12 to 18 months, and assuming we continue inventing on the way, we will match the information processing density of a bacterium, in silicon, around the year 2020. To eclipse this density of bit processing per unit volume, we will most likely have to delve down to individual atoms, and then elemental particles (electrons and protons), and perhaps beyond.

The physical manipulation of individual atoms is crudely possible today, and the reduction of the transistor to a single electron, with some potential beyond, has been demonstrated. Correspondingly, we now understand the processes of chemistry in biological computation and, of course, electronics sufficiently well to postulate and contemplate the creation of a new class of machinery. Here then is the prospect of a major paradigm change—with apologies to Marshall McLuhan. In the future it looks likely that "the message is the molecule." Manipulating individual atoms to create specific structures with great precision, including molecules and smaller, will blur the difference between bits and atoms. Ultimately, they may become the same. This then poses the further prospect of embedded intelligence in everything. If our skin is a smart material, with more processing in a single flake than the most powerful PC so far created, then why not our clothing and other materials?

The most sophisticated of animals, the predators and hunters, have an amazing array of adaptive abilities and unseen technologies at their disposal. From the ultrasonic detection system of bats to the adaptive physical profile of shark skin, distributed SONAR sensors, and electrostatic detector arrays of fish, there appears to be little that we have discovered that has not already evolved. The difference, of course, is the way the solutions are realized. But strikingly, many animals tend to wear their sensory and processing technology as an integral component of their skin.

So far, we describe our engineered solutions in terms of distributed computing, with sensors, transducers, and activators in applications ranging from artificial intelligence to aerospace. In reality these systems are distributions of very discrete blocks of hardware and software, for example, an array of transistors on a chip or a small motorized fin designed to break up and control the onset of turbulent flow over some airfoil. Mother nature adopted the same philosophy but with elements that are much smaller. In this realm the scales of a fish are extreme in size and relatively dumb, where as the adaptability of shark skin has elements 100 to 1000 times smaller and independently smart. In this sense, probably the nearest we have come to emulating nature has been in the active clothing worn by fighter pilots and astronauts and the crude geometric trim adjusters on aircraft wings. Ultimately, really smart materials that communicate at a molecular level could launch new revolutions in healthcare and transport.

95

*"If we had a reliable way
to label our toys good and bad,
it would be easy to regulate
technology wisely."*

Freeman Dyson (1979)

A BAD TECHNOLOGY DAY

Having attended courses on probability and statistics in college, and being a prolific user in industry, I considered myself to be reasonably proficient in their application, until, that is, I discovered Stein's Paradox in a 1970s journal. This was couched as follows: Everything is connected, and correlations between apparently unrelated events can generally be found. This came as a surprise, because the theory as taught mostly assumes (often conveniently) the reverse to be true. In fact, for most practical purposes correlations are so weak they can be ignored. However, Stein demonstrated that car production in Detroit and the Lions football results are related. Similarly, stock prices can be linked to the Olympic athletics results, and so on. How come?

Imagine being a production line worker and your favorite football team wins 28 to 0 against the league champions. The next day, you and your co-workers go into work shoulders back, heads up, in a positive mood. The production line is abuzz with excitement reliving the game, work takes no effort, and production is well above average. That's it, as simple as that. We are influenced in a positive or negative direction by events visible to a significant number of people.

Stein's Paradox recently came to mind again at the end of a bad technology day. Just about everything went wrong. It started when I discovered my mobile phone battery was down to 10 percent charge because it had not seated correctly in the holster. My train was late, and

191

during the journey I discovered a new software bug on my laptop. It was raining in London and I had to wait for a cab, which made me late for my first meeting. I managed to find someone with a mobile phone charger, but while our phones looked identical, he had a newer model with a smaller diameter power jack. So I had to resort to a fixed connection, only to find that the server was down. I tried to call my secretary, but someone had put a backhoe digger through the cable feeding my office. To top it all, my wife called to let me know that the washing machine and vacuum cleaner were broken. And all this was before 12:00 noon.

Quantum theory suggests that all matter in the universe is clustered. But increasingly, it also seems to be true of events. Car accidents, having children, deaths in families, and technology failures seem to support this view. Perhaps there is a quantum theory of life. When I have a bad technology day, I find that careful examination tends to put me, or other people, in the causal driver's seat. An equipment failure can make us tense and prone to error, which leads to mistakes that promote more failures. This catastrophic feedback I can understand and can quantify in an approximate manner, and it is empathic with Stein's Paradox. But I suspect other mechanisms are also at work. Buying all our domestic appliances when we first get married, changing vehicles and IT units at regular intervals: all invoke a rhythm of failure. Most technology is designed for a mean time between failure of about seven years. So this is an identifiable mechanism for synchroncity.

What is puzzling—I cannot find a mechanism or explanation other than the technology autonomously communicating and cooperating—is how diverse, geographically dispersed, and unrelated technologies conspire to create a nightmare of a day about twice a year. This is Stein with a vengeance. Surely the machines are not empathic, are they? I think not, but soon, when they are truly intelligent and on-line, they may be.

96

"There are more ideas on earth than intellectuals imagine. . . . more active, stronger, more resistant, more passionate than politicians think."

Michel Foucault (1978)

MEMES, NOT GENES

When I was a young child, I became infatuated by the idea of messages in bottles cast into the sea. As I recall, this followed a trip to a movie in which some castaway on an island resorted to this desperate mode of communication, and was ultimately rescued. So on vacations I would write, carefully fold, and insert my message into a capped bottle. This I would throw into the sea and watch as it disappeared or returned to shore. Suddenly tide and time were tractable, even to a young mind. The final destination and occasional "return to sender," of course, remained a mystery.

Twenty years later I was lecturing abroad and became aware of the power of the meme. The planting of ideas and concepts with a diverse range of people could bring about change in a very powerful way. I discovered that within organizations, it was insufficient to have an idea and then set about selling it. When you say something new, it may be interesting the first time, and even the second time may still have impact. But say the same thing three of four times and you are either on your soapbox, becoming a bore, or running some private agenda. It's much better to tell lots of people and get them to sell it for you. An idea subsumed into an organizational culture can become established wisdom rather than a personal crusade. It's even better if it penetrates some influential brain so that person can either conceive of your idea, or even invent it in the first place. Then things really start to happen.

The problem with this meme propagation process is the time it takes to socialize and move among a large enough grouping of people to achieve the critical mass necessary for decisions. Twenty years ago, an idea released in the U.S. could take a full year to get back to the UK. Curiously, jokes and political satire would travel across the U.S. and Atlantic in a much shorter time. Very often, a few weeks would be sufficient for such volatile memes to spread across the globe. Really useful ideas, however, were always slower to travel. It was as if speed and longevity was inversely related to usefulness and importance.

Another twenty-five years on and the world has changed significantly. Now I can experimentally insert an idea into a talk in the U.S. and find it buzzing around my laboratory or on my screen by the time I return home. Press, radio, and TV are now faster on the uptake, but faster still is the net. Memes now seem to move at the speed of light to all corners of the planet, and as they do, they often change in nature and form. The originator loses control, and the initial constraints and conditions are lost in a complex and uncontrolled mutation process.

In many respects this all resembles the propagation of genes in carbon life. However, life's evolution depends on genetic mutation between generations to ensure adaptation to environmental pressures. The higher life forms are born fully configured, but minimally preprogrammed with a very basic set of functions. These are progressively enhanced through a relatively slow learning process with parental protection, nurturing, and teaching as the base meme-passing mechanism for each child. Here, then, is a new opportunity for silicon systems. Machines might be able to subsume the experience and knowledge of all previous generations directly, to be assembled, configured, and preprogrammed ready to function as experienced adults. They may then be able to advance at a faster rate, like a radio signal compared to a bottle in the sea.

97

*"Ethics is the art of
recommending to others
the sacrifices required for
cooperation with oneself."*
Bertrand Russell (1976)

MACHINES BEHAVING BADLY?

One of the fundamental questions addressed by the philosophers of ancient Greece was how humankind should live. More than 2000 years later we have a slightly clearer picture and perhaps ought to be addressing new questions with new bounds like: How should companies operate, and how should they employ their technology? While companies are often seen as faceless monoliths, they are made up of people and have a responsibility to shareholders, customers, and society. The capitalist system hinges on the relationship between money and work. We collect tokens as a reward for our labors so we can support ourselves and our families.

Most successful enterprises exhibit a caring response to society and contribute to positive change. But this is not by products and services alone; there are other covert mechanisms at work. In the present maelstrom of business a fully trained and educated workforce is a prerequisite for survival and prosperity. A company attitude of, "we will train no one and rely on the marketplace to supply our needs," coupled with, "I went to university and I am now educated for life," are a recipe for disaster. Continual training and education are now the hallmark of the successful, along with teamwork, dedication to quality, and a total customer focus.

Today, the most successful companies spend 10 percent or more of their resources on people training and education. This most likely involves a time commitment at home and at work for employees and the provision of equipment, materials, and time by the employer. But there is a new type of company and corporation coming. They will employ no one, require only occasional human attention, and will trade bits at breakneck speed. They will have no need to train or educate people because people will be irrelevant to their operation.

In the extreme case peopleless companies will be distributed globally and may even be off-planet, with servers mounted on satellites. What will they do? They will be the new bit traders. Machines that sell communication bandwidth, bit storage space, trade in bit futures, and sell software and services without human intervention are already at an early trial stage. But why should we be contemplating and even looking forward to the advent of noncarbon companies? Put simply, they are needed to sustain the growth of services and commerce and make them available to a global population that is becoming increasingly polarized between the haves and have-nots. It is essential that the bit business become like the rain, essentially free, or at least so low-cost that it seems free.

People are incredibly expensive and are the major expense of most organizations. If we are to see the continued exponential fall in costs in the major technology-based service and supply sectors, people have to be replaced with machines. But in any case, humans can no more service the entire population for future services as they could replace all the telephone switches with manual operators, or all the computers with mechanical adding machines. But more significantly, the planet could not provide all the physical resources either.

So the question now arises. Will peopleless companies have codes of ethics, and look after and care for the human population? For sure they will, but only if we program them to do so. We are reaching a point where strains of new technology require built-in rules and responsibilities, a recognition of what is important and vital to the human race. As they get more intelligent and powerful, they will make decisions on their own account. Perhaps we need a few more philosophers asking an even more fundamental question: How should machines behave?

98

"Man has lost the basic skill of the ape, the ability to scratch its back. Which gave it extraordinary independence, and the liberty to associate for reasons other than the need for mutual back-scratching."

Jean Baudrillard (1987)

WRITING OFF SKILLS

At birth we come preprogrammed with respiratory, vascular, and all essential life functions operational. We also instinctively mouth for food, hang onto fur, skin, or the branch of a tree. But in contrast to other species, walking necessitates years of practice. It also seems to be a function we continually adapt as our bodily characteristics change with age, food intake, clothing, and whatever we carry. If we suffer an accident and undergo weeks of traction in the hospital, we not only suffer muscular atrophy and a stiffening of the joints, we also seem to forget how to walk. Even more than riding a bike or swimming, walking seems to be a function that needs continual practice and adaptation. Such natural functions are now augmented by a vast range of artificial abilities like reading, writing, typing, and programming technology.

The stark need for basic skills reinforcement first became evident to me as a young adult when I was ill and unable to walk for a couple of weeks. Curiously, the recovery period exceeded the disability time. More recently, skill reinforcement again came to the fore as I returned to fly fishing after an absence of 25 years. It took hours of practice to regain the ability to cast a line effectively.

Even more dramatically, I was recently called upon to write, with a pen, just a sentence or two in short bursts on diverse topics for a wide and rapidly changing audience. To my surprise, I found that I had lost the skill. Yes, I could scribble fairly illegibly on any topic at great speed, and certainly I could type what was required. But write in copper plate? I just could not do it; I had lost the ability. Quite literally, I had to take time out to practice the increasingly irrelevant art of scratching on paper with a pointy stick.

These cumulative experiences prompted me to think of my changing skill set and the accelerating losses our species is experiencing. Most of us need not worry about tracking and hunting down prey; making traps and snares and weapons from stone, sticks, and animal sinews; or skinning, gutting, cleaning, and cooking food on an open fire. But how about computer programs or technology interfaces? Trying to work on some five-year-old files recently, I found myself struggling to modify the content. I had lost the basic skills needed. Even more dramatically, I came across my old scientific pocket calculator that had gone unused for only six years. Now this was a machine I had lived with for a long time. It predated my first laptop. I inserted new batteries in the expectation of being able to use it with ease. To say the least, I was rusty, and what had been simple for me years ago was now very difficult.

I well remember an old comedian claiming that he could only read, but not write. In Japan this is now becoming a truism for some young people. Hours of practice are needed to form the basic Japanese set of over 3000 characters, and along with students in many other cultures, young people's writing abilities significantly lag their reading skills. With the rising use of computers, the young are now focusing on what is more essential and pressing for their future. No computer skills, no job is the key worry. Perhaps for most of us this trend will accelerate with the use of talk and type programs. Why write when you can type and/or talk? Why do anything if a machine can do it for us, and do it better?

99

A WORD PROCESSOR THAT WORKS

*The machines that are first invented . . .
are always the most complex, and
succeeding artists generally discover
that . . . with fewer wheels . . . than
had originally been employed, the same
effects may be more easily produced.*

Adam Smith (1795)

Every now and again, some accident of technology forces me in an unusual direction to experience something new, and sometimes old. On a recent overseas trip my word processing package delivered a crippling blow by developing a very peculiar fault at 35,000 ft. On every carriage return it would create a new copy of either the line I was working on or the page, or complete document, or everything at once. This occurred at the start of a five-day excursion, with little chance of a wide bandwidth connection for on-line repairs. Fortunately, I had a standby word processor produced by an entirely different company on my hard drive. In a matter of minutes I was back in action typing another in this series of monologues.

It is amazing how we are so easily conditioned by the second rate if force-fed a diet of technology dictated by a need to interface with the rest of the world and compliance within our companies and organizations. What a delight—a word processor that is clean and uncluttered to look at, intuitive and easy to use, extremely fast and responsive, very light on memory, and as solid as a rock. I could instantly find all the facilities I needed and didn't seem to be missing anything. What have I been doing? Why have I been suffering all these years? Suddenly I seem another 10 percent more productive, and hey, this word processor allows me to translate to and from just about every format or package I ever heard of, including my old one.

It gets better. This new package requires only 30 percent of the memory normally devoted to my word processor. It simultaneously occupies less hard disc and demands less RAM, and runs at something approaching twice the speed at my human interface level. It opens up and saves faster, spell-checks, word-counts, corrects, backs up, and formats instantly. What an absolute joy, a technology that matches me and my lust for speed.

Somewhere in all of this, there is a gradual feeling of familiarity. I seem to have been here before, but a long time ago. I'm pretty sure this is a more updated version of my original word processor that arrived on a single floppy disc well over a decade ago. It is now flooding back to me; this is where I first learned word processing—no handbooks, no training courses to attend, because there was never any need or demand for them, just good design. What have we done? Why have we allowed mediocre technology to take over? Surely we have not rolled over just to appease the gods of corporate and global compatibility.

In this new package I now discover an equally delightful spread-sheet and graphics package with all the facilities I need and similar economies of memory and speed. Perhaps office suites are like video recorders: the best do not, or cannot, win, because the market just goes with dominance and ease of compatibility. Perhaps we have to wait until a technology is so crushingly bad that there is a rebellion. For sure, there seem to be some very attractive alternatives to the packages I have been using to date.

The next five days following this incident were crucial in steering me to make a bold decision. Not only would I continue my personal policy of not operating with a standard PC platform, but I would not run the standard sets of software either. It is just too tough when there are such wonderful alternatives available. Why ride a motorbike if a car is cheaper?

100

*"Reality is the stuff
that doesn't go away
just because you stop
believing in it."*

Philip K. Dick (1997)

WHERE HAS THE REALITY GONE?

How is it we are able to become emotionally involved in a film or a drama production on TV and yet we find video conferencing and CD ROM images alien? Children complain of "blocky" CD images, and we might detect that jerky motion as the football streaks across the screen, left to right. Where has the reality gone? We start with 100 percent reality, and then we make it digital. But this is not the problem per se, for the digital form ensures longevity and almost perfect reproduction independent of transmission distance and storage time. The reality disappears in a quest to squeeze more and more information into fixed pipes and storage volumes. When bandwidth and storage are expensive, it is obviously sensible to compress the signal. However, when optical fiber and CDs are plentiful, then so is bandwidth, and we can afford to transmit and store signals at much greater bit rates and detail.

Reality degradation is perhaps most evident in today's video conferencing terminals. These are remarkable pieces of electronic engineering that present reasonable images transmitted over ISDN circuits at 128 kbit/s and higher rates. They allow telemeetings across the planet that are effective for many businesses, medical, and education applications, but you would not try courting a lover on this medium. They would appear inhuman, devoid of appeal, a mere facsimile of their true persona, presented on the wrong scale, in a blocky distorted manner, and off-color. It is extremely difficult to sell someone a car or propose marriage when your eyes are perceived to be looking over the top of their head. Eye contact, gaze awareness, and body language are all important components for effective human communication. Real-time movement—coordinated hand, eye, and voice— are also key elements for realism. Interestingly, high quality sound creates the illusion of enhancing the visual image in the human mind, a fact that has been totally neglected in telecommunications, but not by Hollywood.

Digital compression to save bandwidth brings with it a processing delay that is increasing rapidly. A single photon can now traverse the planet on an optical fiber in a shorter time than it takes a GSM phone to convert a speaker's voice into a digital signal. Perversely, switching and routing systems now add to this problem with uncontrolled delays necessary to efficiently pack all time slots and save bandwidth. When your image and your voice arrive late, become detached, have an unreal jerky, blocky quality, and you sound as if you are talking down a cardboard tube, communication suffers.

Until we create large wall-size screens with daylight brightness and high contrast, we will continue to drive that car, ride that train, and board that airplane. The only people who like to travel are those who don't do it. There is little glamour and joy to be gained trekking from one country, city, town, and company to another. To really make a dent in the numbers of people traveling and the damage to our environment, we need to overcome the limitations of coding, bandwidth, and display technology.

Optical fiber and storage systems can provide sufficient bandwidth for the accurate reproduction of the acoustic and visual. But so far, a solution for lifelike display has eluded us, and we need something revolutionary beyond the paradigm of television. Perhaps we have to wait for the holographic projector to realize that true sense of being there and that real presence of human contact. Until then, we either travel or try to become emotionally involved with rather blocky, nasal, and artificially distant beings.

101

*"Probably the only place
where a man can feel
really secure is in a
maximum security prison . . . "*
Germaine Greer (1970)

COMMON SENSE SECURITY

According to the media and popular wisdom, the two greatest hazards of the Internet are pornography and security. I have no idea why this is so, or how these myths have become dominant concerns of the press and primary inhibitors for new and established businesses to enter the world of electronic commerce. The reality is that better quality pornography is available from book shops (so they tell me!), and the net is inherently more secure than the world it is replacing. Of course, there is a proviso, and it is: we should not be stupid.

Secure Internet sites are available for children and provide a high degree of protection from undesirable material and people. In general, this protection is far more effective than that afforded in the world of paper, audio and video tape, radio, and TV. On the security front the situation is even better. There has not been a single recorded instance of anyone having his or her card number intercepted on the net and being defrauded, which is more than can be said of the coins, notes, checks, and plastic world.

On a recent train journey, I handed a passenger my business card on which I had written his name, address, credit card number, and bank branch details. He instantly demanded to know where I had got this sensitive information. I looked him in the eye and said, "When you use a mobile phone, you shout." He was not amused, but the other passengers were. Electronic crime does not demand fancy technology, just opportunism.

For many people making a purchase by giving someone your charge card details over the telephone or Internet is seen as risky and very insecure. Why? Because they have been told it is so. But these same people buy gas, food, and goods from stores and hand over their plastic to a stranger who makes a paper copy, asks for their signature, and retains the whole—no questions asked, not a thought about security. At street cash machines people stand well back so you can see them enter their PIN, and cast their paper receipt to the floor. What wonderful opportunities for the thief. These people then declare uncertainty and worry about the net, fostered by an unthinking media.

Most security failures can be traced to human fallibility, bribery, and corruption. Granted, electronic break-ins are on the increase, but so is the theft of complete machines, the violation of offices, paper records, and mail. So in what respect is the e-world so different? Well, only in its scale and apparent invisibility. E-working now dominates the developed world, and crime will naturally follow, so we should take sensible precautions, not be prompted to overreact by the scare stories of the uninformed. Who would leave the door of their home unlocked? Then we should not leave computers wide open to attack via some unlocked networked access.

Entire legal systems stand or fall by pen and ink; the human signature is legally binding. It is also very easy to forge. Paper money, gold, and silver are easy to steal, but require physical action that is visible. E-crime, on the other hand, can introduce new dimensions of reach, scale, and anonymity, and we should be careful. Of course, we can reduce the odds against e-crime by applying countermeasures, with regularly changing passwords and code sequences, but this can rapidly become expensive and inconvenient. Personally, I prefer multiple low-cost and very simple protection methods, including network disconnection when not active, light encryption, passwords, and locked files. But most of all, I rely on common sense.

102

"Television thrives on unreason, and unreason thrives on television. It strikes at the emotions rather than the intellect."

Sir Robin Day (1989)

THEY JUST DON'T GET IT

Without exception, every European institution I get involved with thinks in terms of the regulation and control of information and the Internet. This is in stark contrast to the U.S., where talk always centers on the freedom and exploitation of mass networking. From government to education and broadcasting, it is as if the Europeans really just do not get IT. All they see is a threat that should be regulated, controlled, and suppressed. The reality is that they may as well try and herd cats. The Internet is naturally out of and hopefully beyond control.

The old universities, schools, broadcasters, network providers, regulators, agencies, and legal establishments are alarmed at the concept of no control. It may be that they begrudge the concept of 100 percent customer access, choice, and control, but I suspect they just don't comprehend. They seem to have become so dogged by history and tradition, so engrained in established paradigms, they cannot conceive of any other way. Worse still, they seem fundamentally incapable of thinking out of their box.

Public broadcasters often argue that they are the last bastion of free speech and therefore an absolute necessity for a civilized future. Recent attempts by one media group to prevent the publishing of a book that would have been politically contentious in southeast Asia certainly supports this argument. However, there are many more counterexamples, including the suppression of the identity of a UK Minister's son who had been involved with drugs. Of course, the basis of this attempt at information control was the greater public good, whatever that is. Fortunately, this containment action was side-stepped by the Internet, which made all the information public and freely available for weeks before the old media could reveal the name. Curiously, the name was widely known in the media of just about every other country on the planet except the UK. It therefore seems that the Internet is more about free speech than broadcasting or newspapers.

The question now arises: Will the noncontrollist mentality play in the business world? Will net activity be taxable and censored, or will it be totally free of government control? Is it possible to conceive of a world where bits are free and atoms are not? I think so, and I think it to be essential. But to make it work, we need a new business model, a new way of creating the wealth necessary to sustain the physical infra-structure and well-being of societies. And I don't think such a model will emerge from Europe; we will have to look toward North America. The "new world" is far more likely to create a newer world than the old. As Europe continues to debate and think control and tax, the U.S. leg-islates for freedom.

I often hear people state that no one is making money on the Internet. Well, by the same token, no one makes money on the tele-phone, radio, or billboards either. Clearly, none of this is strictly true. The Internet is already contributing billions of dollars worth of trade to the global economy as a new and increasingly essential communica-tions medium. Critically, it is also the first time direct bit sales have been possible. Information transmitted over all previous media mere-ly prompted some human action that earned money. On the net bits are available for sale directly for the first time, with no human inter-mediary or action. At the extremes machines trade in their own right, making money with minimal human help, and they can operate from anywhere, even from a satellite off-planet. Perhaps this will be the first free trade zone.

103

*"In the middle ages
anyone could be a physicist—
all you needed was a pointy hat!"*

Alan Kay (1997)

A WORLD OF NOTHING

We live in a physical domain where things appear to be solid, of manageable dimensions and spacing comparable to the human form and mind. Broadly speaking, everything we see, feel, hear, smell, and taste is bounded by about 12 orders of magnitude. However, travel into outer space or down into the depths of atoms and the dominant material is nothing, just emptiness. Solidity is actually hard to find. Here, there are many more orders of magnitude difference spanning these domains. For us, this is counterintuitive, since our senses and practical experience lead us to perceive and think in terms of a solidity, of finite space and physical limits to what we might do. The smallest thing we can see with the naked eye is only slightly smaller than $10EXP(-4)$ m, that is 0.0001 m, and with an optical microscope around $10EXP(-7)$ m. Using an atom smasher, the smallest objects detected are w and z particles of about $10EXP(-17)$ m diameter. Conversely, the largest man-made objects, and those of nature, range in the tens or thousands of meters. At the other extreme, the largest detected clusters of galaxies in the universe span some $10EXP25$ m diameter. From the smallest to the largest, the span is some 42 orders of magnitude, compared to our very limited 12 or so.

So what percentage of space is more than nothing? Well, it depends on precisely how we form an estimate, but the critical density of the universe is about 3 hydrogen atoms per cubic meter, that is, $4.8 \times 10EXP(-27)$ kg/m³. So on average, all space is very empty. In terms of volume there is a factor of 10EXP(9) of emptiness, that is, 1,000,000,000 parts of nothing and only 1 part of something. Clearly, nothing (emptiness) dominates, and we have a lot of vacant space to exploit.

This has important implications for the future of everything. For example, we currently minimize the weight of aircraft, automobiles, and bridge structures by removing material from areas that do not experience significant stress. In the crudest realizations we just drill or mill out large holes with rounded profiles to reduce the incidence and risk of stress cracks. But if we could manipulate the space in materials more efficiently, at an atomic and molecular level, then we could perhaps reduce the weight of an aircraft by 90 percent and yet make it much stronger.

Every piece of technology has to live with and accommodate material imperfections that limit physical strength, bit storage, processing, and display. If we could eradicate imperfections, we would see dramatic performance improvements, with reductions in manufacturing cost, wasted material, energy, and time. While bulk science has served us well with clean rooms offering less than one particle in a million contamination, production materials are still subject to the random placement of atoms compounded by impurities that ultimately limit the performance of our technology. If we could build electronic and photonic devices an atom at a time, we might see another technological leap on a par with the change from the thermionic valve to the transistor.

To perfect nanotechnology and microrobotics, to build devices an atom at a time, and to get their type and geometry precise relative to their peers may be vital steps for the future. It looks feasible to enhance many of our technologies at least a millionfold over the projections we currently hold to be true. We also stand to discover many new and unthought of properties. For example, every atom could be engineered to represent at least one bit, and so atoms would equal bits.

104

"My sole inspiration is a telephone call from a director."

Cole Porter (1955)

Now and again someone takes my breath away with a monumental statement lacking any understanding of a technology-dominated world. Most recently, it was a pundit on the perils and dangers of the telephone and how we could live without it. Alexander Graham Bell's 1876 patent was a spinoff from his work on telegraph systems and speech therapy with the deaf. It was his refinement of the fixed-magnet earphone that realized the first telephone. And no one could have guessed the demands and advances this would trigger that now underpin human existence.

A world without telephones would be devoid of microphones, earphones, and loudspeakers. Why? Because as soon as these modules are realized, the telephone is both possible and inevitable. So imagine a world without radio and TV, only silent movies, and no computers. Why no computers? Without the telephone Strowger would not have invented the automatic switch, and so Colossus (the WWII code-breaking computer) and other early computers could not have been built. More critically, without the development of electromechanics and the simplest of electronic components, we would have been unable to automate the production processes that are key to the creation of a viable electronics industry.

Without the demands from telephone and radio broadcasting networks, we would not have developed thermionic valves to their height of perfection. Most likely, they would have been concentrated on telegraph radio stations and copper line regenerators. Nor would we have the transistor or integrated circuit. We would have no coaxial cables, optical fiber, lasers, microwave radio, satellites, or the space race. We would be living in an early Victorian world, with master and servant, telegraph systems and copper cables, messenger boys and telegrams, a world much slower than today, unable to sustain a population now fast heading to 6Bn.

The music and entertainment industry would be puny—no amplifiers, no radio, hi-fi, tapes, or CDs, just plastic cylinders and discs scratching out their music with diamond-tipped pins feeding acoustic horns mounted on wonder boxes. There would be no pop industry, just the rich and privileged getting to see and hear opera and orchestras. There would be no TV, VHS, camcorders, computer games, or pocket calculators, PDAs, laptops, or PCs. Offices would be dominated by paper, typing pools, and business subject to the delays of the postal network.

International travel would be for only a few on aircraft a far cry from today's jumbo jets. Train, shipping, and aircraft would be organized over telegraph wires and primitive wireless. Travel schedules would be strictly rationed by limited and expensive bit transport. There would be a lack of trained telegraph operators, bottlenecks of information, ignorant populations starved of information, dictatorships, and empires.

The planet would be polluted, consuming ever more hydrocarbons to support incredibly inefficient manufacturing and logistic systems. Our science, technology, and basic understanding would be limited by crude technologies produced without electronics. There would be no radio telescopes, no scanning electron microscopes, no medical scanners, accurate timekeeping, or significant advance in materials and production techniques.

A partial insight into this hypothetical state can be glimpsed by visiting the third world. With no telephones travel is difficult. You cannot book a ticket for train, boat, or plane without traveling to the ticket office. When your plane takes off, the destination has no idea of your status until you are within 100 miles or so. The supply and delivery of food, clothing, heat, light, power, and water we take for granted is then critical as life becomes survival.

Those who complain about technology enjoy the comfort and convenience it affords them, but they do not understand. Life without technology is tough. Alexander Graham Bell helped the deaf, but his legacy to humankind is enormous, much bigger than most can imagine.

105

*"The advantage of
the emotions is that
they lead us astray."*
Oscar Wilde (1891)

EMOTIONAL TECHNOLOGY

My youngest son received an unusual alarm clock for Christmas, and over the vacation period he played and became expert at adjusting this present. Having proved its trustworthiness in daytime trials, he carefully set this electronic wonder to go off at 7:00 a.m. on the morning of his first day back at school. As expected, it started its lengthy musical verse at exactly 7:00 on the day. Hitting the snooze button instantly returned it to a quiet state. A few minutes later, the alarm started again, only this time with harsher and louder music. This process was repeated several times until my son exclaimed, "It is getting angry. I'd better get up." The emotional alarm clock has arrived.

While our emotional communication is complex and little understood, this alarm clock experience prompted some conjecture on the possibilities for emotion-sensing by IT in general. If machines could sense our state, what would they do, and could they improve our lot? My only direct experience has been the passive mouse and some interactive spacecraft manuals.

In the former case the worst possible tactile feedback comes into play when standing before an expectant audience trying to line up a projector or some demonstration. If all goes well, there is no problem. But at the first hint of trouble, the hands start to sweat and the electrostatic coupling between finger and electronics starts to break down. This causes more tension and more sweat, and even worse coupling, and a rapid worsening of this vital control function. An inexorable downward spiral starts with evermore negative feedback. My only solution to date is to quickly wipe all moisture from my hands.

In the latter case, I was observing some adolescents voice-navigating a CD spacecraft manual, when one of them uttered a profanity. The machine responded with the stern words, "Do you really think you should address me in that way?" The impact was profound, and the discourse that followed was noticeably more polite.

We often associate the word emotion with an unenviable, illogical, dangerous, and unthinking human condition. However, the latest research seems to point to emotions being a vital ingredient to sensible decision making. It turns out to be one of those valuable human qualities we often deride but would miss if it were banished. This then begs the question: Would machines and other objects benefit from emotions? If they could identify ours and use them to communicate with us, it might prove extremely valuable.

A very simple facility I have on my machines is the change of screen color by memory state. With ample RAM available, the screen is deep blue, but as RAM gets low, there is a transition to lighter shades of blue. As RAM becomes critical, the shade goes to pink, and it is time to take action. The next phase in this direction is a serious crash. What a simple but powerful icon, and what a pity there is no reciprocal path allowing machines to gauge my emotional state. If only they could slow down and speed up, bring in help files, and give me warnings as I make tension- and fatigue-related errors.

My wish list for emotional IT would include my car seat, office and home chairs and furniture, plus keyboard and mouse with an ability to detect my temperature, perspiration, respiration, muscle tension, and other states. Messages and responses with a sense of urgency, or mood-sensitive environments with relaxing music, lighting, tones, and temperatures would be a real boon, not to mention the possibility of early warnings from other humans.

106

"If the Lord Almighty had consulted me before embarking upon Creation, I should have recommended something simpler."

Alfonso X, King of Castile and Leon (1221–1284)

BITS, ENERGY, AND LIFE

Established theory, wisdom, and belief supposes life either started by some divine intervention or by electrical storms creating the necessary amino acids in pools on the earth's surface. Of course, either version requires the existence of the fundamental hydrocarbons and a long evolution time to mutate and migrate across the planet. But it seems that a more likely scenario starts deep in the oceans. Go a mile or two down in the deepest waters and there is a richness of life that far exceeds any rain forest.

Sulphuric acid bubbles violently out of volcanic vents at about 400 °C to create a highly toxic mix with deep ocean salt water at 4 °C. This mix is so toxic to us that there is no legal way we could get a permit to dump waste of equal toxicity into the ocean. And yet there are worms and crabs in great numbers and variety feeding off a layer of white bacteria that lies inches thick over vast expanses of the seabed surrounding these vents. All of this seemingly spewed out at high pressure with no electricity or light to prime the life process, and certainly no photosynthesis to sustain life. Moreover, the volcanic activity in these deep subocean ridges regularly destroys these islands of life. But within weeks more bacteria seems to originate from new and multiple vents. It is as if life itself pours out of the rocks by some chemical process we do not yet understand. So perhaps the keyline of creation should be, "Let there be heat, or more specifically, let there be energy." And perhaps any form of energy will do.

No doubt, we will one day discover the truth by unraveling the mystery of life in all its glorious and intricate detail, and then go on to recreate the very conditions necessary to trigger and sustain new and original life. For now the race is on, and it is between carbon and silicon, test tube and computer. If all it takes to create life is the essential chemicals and heat, and remembering heat is just energy, which is merely the transformation of matter, then it begs the question: Is their an equivalent in the silicon world? Well, it would seem to be that the right bits, connectivity, and dynamic disorder—chaos—could be all that is needed. A single embracing descriptor for both situations is entropy. The state of disorder between atoms or bits should do the trick.

If this is the case, it is only a question of time before we create life by design or accident. When we do, what will we have become, and what will we do, and how will this knowledge change us? For sure, it does not promote us to god status, but it does load us with a new and fundamental responsibility. This new knowledge will make us unbelievably powerful. The crude ability we already have to genetically control, steer, and modify life is already creating challenging results. More responsibility will come as we go beyond genetic tinkering.

Only 1000 years ago, all of humankind, their livestock, and pets represented just 0.1 percent of the vertebrate life mass on the planet. By 2050, if we do nothing but survive, this number will exceed 85 percent. And if our computers spring to life and join us, our livestock and pets, we will then represent 99.9 percent . In just 1000 years the balance of life on planet earth will have been inverted by us and our technology, and evolution will have taken a giant leap.

107

*"It is only the enlightened ruler . . .
who will use the highest intelligence . . .
for the purposes of spying, and
thereby they achieve great results."*

Sun Tzu (ca. 490 B.C.)

EYES AND EARS IN THE SKY

More than eight years ago I managed to get my hands on one of the first miniature CCD cameras, about the size of a shirt button. This I mounted in a badge that I wore at public lectures for the sole purpose of a surprise demonstration. When I got to the end of my lecture, which featured the miniaturization of technology, someone would always ask a question. I would respond by walking into the audience to get as close as I could to the subject, at which point I would activate the hidden camera with a concealed switch. The questioner would suddenly be projected onto the screen behind me, and as I then moved about the audience, people would try to guess where the camera was located. Often it would take a few people some time to figure out I was the cameraman.

Since that time miniature cameras have become even more miniaturized, more available, less power-hungry, and have far better definition and sensitivity. They are commonly used in banks, retail stores, streets, parks, and public buildings, and some are worn by the police and emergency services. Cameras are now everywhere, present little threat to our privacy, enhance our security, and result in few surprises.

More recently I was at a conference where Paul McCready, the gossamer condor designer, walked onto the stage with a model airplane with a wingspan of only 70 cm. The house lights were turned up and the aircraft came alive. Solar cells provide the power for two electric motors, a miniature camera, and a radio system. He flew this almost silent aircraft around the auditorium powered only by the house lights, at speeds up to 50 km/h, at the same-time taking real time video of the audience. He then pulled a 15 cm version from his coat and repeated the demonstration minus the miniature camera, which was too heavy for this frame. Finally came an ornocopter, which looked like an insect and weighed only 1 g. This was a rubberband-powered flying machine of 10 cm wingspan that flew like a fly, with flapping wings. It took off, flew to the top of the auditorium, and then disappeared out of a vent. This was an amazing amalgam of new technologies and presented solutions looking for problems.

I was immediately prompted to ask the most obvious of questions: What could this technology be used for and what are the implications? Well, military drones for gun control, logistic observation, arms and border control, and even low-cost missiles are obvious applications. In the civil arena they would clearly make ideal observation and control platforms for our congested roads, fishery protection, or for scanning accident and disaster sites. But how about sporting events? Low-noise, low-visibility units could fly above some arena so we could enjoy a birds-eye view. And perhaps we could even afford individual control to a limited audience. But what else? How about aerial platforms for radio and optical repeater stations, facilitating communication across a city or town, between villages, or hopping over mountains and giving access to remote locations. A new range of low-cost toys also looks possible that the technologically literate could buy and launch for fun or other purposes.

Perhaps the most radical step promoted by this technology will be the creation of successively miniaturized flying platforms with sensors and intelligence. Flying robots have arrived, and soon we will all be able to afford eyes and ears in the air anywhere. Now these will really impact on privacy, and I suspect we are also going to need a new raft of regulations and controls.

108

*"Space isn't remote at all.
It's only an hour's
drive away if your car
could go straight upwards."*

Sir Fred Hoyle (1979)

TIME TRAVELERS

We have been preoccupied by travel and discovery since we first became true bipeds. For the vast majority of our history, we have been concerned with, and constrained to, traveling through space. Time only became an issue when physical travel exceeded our speed of communication. Not until the arrival of the steam train did we find it necessary to invent the telegraph, which in turn led to the telephone, radio, and TV. Today, time is a primary concern, for we have conquered all aspects of terrestrial travel, barring the logistics of making it sustainably efficient. We can travel anywhere and even escape the planet, but time is always running out. Non of us has enough time.

Most life systems inherently try to be efficient; they seek out the lowest energy route to the greatest return. They do this unthinkingly, as it is part of the natural order, like a leaf falling. And so it is with us. Most have enough space and resources to travel, but time is nonnegotiable. It is always limited and cannot be reversed or replayed. The passage of time also seems to speed up each year we live as we pack our lives with increasing activity and experience. How then might we become even more efficient in the use of this nontransmutable commodity? Might time travel be possible through some artificial dilation and expansion at least?

Time spent on a keyboard produces a huge dilation of time. It is even worse than reading a book. For me, looking at the screen for 10 minutes yields one hour of nonscreen time slipping by unnoticed. Say to your family that you only need 10 minutes to do your mail or finish this little job, and you emerge from the screen an hour or two later to frowns of perplexity. On the upside this dilation can be used to great effect in the reverse direction. When traveling by car, train, boat, or air, open up your laptop for the duration, expand from 12 to 16 point to off-set motion sickness, and a 1-hour trip becomes 10 minutes, a 7-hour journey about 60 minutes. Traveling across the Atlantic only takes an hour, the Pacific two hours, and so on, and work is completed without the conscious sacrifice that it so often takes.

Now a new and irrational phenomenon enters our lives. Waiting for a bus or train for 10 or 15 minutes is irritating and wasteful. But think about a reboot, download, or application startup. These seconds feel like a substantial period of time. When your computer is powering up, you might as well be powered down. But we don't have that luxury; we can only wait ineffectively. The only solution is more RAM, faster processors, better power handling, and more efficient and smarter soft-ware. We need machines on 24 hours a day, all applications open simul-taneously, and no lockups or reboots.

When traveling by air, train, or car, I avoid reading newspapers and watching free videos. Similarly, when staying in hotels, I avoid watching TV. Instead of letting work pile up back at home and office, I time travel—work full-time on the move. When I do get back to base I try to hit the ground running. Time dilation has been used and not wasted. I feel ultraefficient. But is there a downside? Well, a bit like a fighter pilot or someone on a rollercoaster ride, nausea is the challenge. Seven hours of information flow may feel like an hour on the body, but rather more on the mind. We are the ultimate limiters.

INDEX

ABOUT THE AUTHOR

Peter Cochrane is Head of Research at British Telecommunications Laboratories, devoted to the exploration of future technologies, systems, networks and services, and is widely recognized as Great Britain's foremost technology theorist. A member of the New York Academy of Sciences and visiting professor at several universities, Cochrane is also on the Advisory Board of CSC Index, one of the world's largest management consultancies. He writes a weekly column in the *Daily Telegraph* and contributes regularly to the *Financial Times*, *Wired* and *Guardian*.

Visit him on the web at
www.labs.bt.com/people/cochrap